VOCABULARY IN CONTEXT

The

History of

Hip Hop

The First 25 Years

Prestwick House

VOCABULARY IN CONTEXT:
THE HISTORY OF HIP-HOP—THE FIRST 25 YEARS

Senior Editor:

Paul Moliken

Cover and Text Design:

Chris Koniencki

Layout and Production:

Jeremy Clark

Prestwick House

P.O. Box 658 • Clayton, DE 19938
(800) 932-4593 • www.prestwickhouse.com

ISBN: 978-1-62019-341-9
Item: 310580

TABLE OF CONTENTS

Rap's Wrongs 1

The Roots of Rap 9

"Rapper's Delight" 17

Rapper/Movie Star 25

Hip-Hop Culture 33

Chuck D and Flav 41

The Beasties 49

Freestyle 57

Dr. Dre 65

East Coast/West Coast 73

Tupac 81

Hip-Hop's Firsts 89

Jay-Z 97

Female Rappers 105

The Queen 113

Slim Shady 121

Dogg in the House 129

Vocabulary 137

RAP'S WRONGS

HIP-HOP IS AMONG the most innovative, important, and influential art forms of the last 40 years. Its music has broken new ground while also honoring musical traditions and pioneers of the past. Its lyrics have been considered by some to be a form of great modern-day poetry. Perhaps, above all, hip-hop has provided a new medium for creativity. It gives a voice to those who have felt voiceless.

At the same time, in American society, hip-hop has been a source of debate and division. Many have strongly criticized the content of rap lyrics, much of which encourages drug use and violence and promotes disrespect for women. Critics point to the dangerous and illegal behaviors of some rap artists. These critics further argue that rap and hip-hop have the effect of **inciting** bloodshed and encouraging sexist attitudes. The result has been that hip-hop has become the **pariah**—the unwelcome outcast—of the music world.

Over the years, there have been numerous attempts to **censor** the profanity in rap lyrics. Critics point to the negative messages and themes in the lyrics, arguing that much of rap music **glorifies** the "gangsta" lifestyle. **Felonies** like assault and drug use are shown in a positive light. Some lyrics try to persuade listeners to rebel against authority. Other lyrics also create conflict within the hip-hop community itself. Deadly feuds have developed among the artists and between competing record labels; the East Coast/West Coast rivalry, which is covered in its own chapter, was a dispute that led to the deaths of Biggie Smalls and Tupac Shakur.

Rap has also caused dangerous and illegal behavior in an indirect way. Fans have committed crimes in an effort to gain the same types of reputations as their idols (or the personalities that the artists project in their lyrics). Many people believe that rap is the **bane** of law enforcement because of the problems it creates.

Another criticism of rap music is the negative portrayal of women, in addition to the **misogyny** encouraged in some rap lyrics. Male **chauvinism** and attitudes of superiority lead many male rappers to characterize women as inferior. Some rappers talk about women as though they were material things to be acquired and owned. Studies have found that when women are objectified in this way, violence against them increases. The way the men devalue women **begets** greater oppression and mistreatment. Furthermore, romantic relationships and **fidelity** are often devalued in rap music.

Hip-hop artists sometimes convey the message in their songs that social status is measured primarily through the possession of material goods. Many lyrics and music videos show rappers **flaunting** their expensive cars, large homes, jewelry, clothing, and cash. A few artists have even **capitalized** on materialism by starting their own clothing lines. As a result, young-adult listeners may shift their values from education and personal growth to the attainment of wealth.

One cannot deny the negative effects rap has on real life, despite its positive qualities. Rap music alters notions of what is considered acceptable behavior in society. Readers of *The History of Hip-Hop* are encouraged, therefore, to focus on rap as an art form and social commentary, not as a way to live their lives.

EXERCISE 1 / WORD LIST

Use the context in which the word is used to determine what the word probably means. Write a brief definition in the space provided.

1. **bane:** _____

   Rap has also caused dangerous and illegal behavior in an indirect way. Fans have committed crimes in an effort to gain the same types of reputations as their idols (or the personalities that the artists project in their lyrics). Many people believe that rap is the **bane** of law enforcement because of the problems it creates.

2. **beget:** _____

   The way the men devalue women **begets** greater oppression and mistreatment.

3. **capitalize:** _____

   A few artists have even **capitalized** on materialism by starting their own clothing lines.

4. **censor:** _____

   Over the years, there have been numerous attempts to **censor** the profanity in rap lyrics. Critics point to the negative messages and themes in the lyrics, arguing that much of rap music glorifies the "gangsta" lifestyle.

5. **chauvinism:** _____

   Male **chauvinism** and attitudes of superiority lead many male rappers to characterize women as inferior.

6. **felony:** _____

   Felonies like assault and drug use are shown in a positive light.

7. **fidelity:** _____

   Furthermore, romantic relationships and **fidelity** are often devalued in rap music.

8. **flaunt:** _____

   Many lyrics and music videos show rappers **flaunting** their expensive cars, large homes, jewelry, clothing, and cash.

9. **glorify:** _____

Over the years, there have been numerous attempts to censor the profanity in rap lyrics. Critics point to the negative messages and themes in the lyrics, arguing that much of rap music **glorifies** the "gangsta" lifestyle.

10. **incite:** _____

These critics further argue that rap and hip-hop have the effect of **inciting** bloodshed and encouraging sexist attitudes.

11. **misogyny:** _____

Another criticism of rap music is the negative portrayal of women, in addition to the **misogyny** encouraged in some rap lyrics.

12. **pariah:** _____

The result has been that hip-hop has become the **pariah**—the unwelcome outcast—of the music world.

EXERCISE 2 / USING WORDS IN CONTEXT

Fill in the blank with the vocabulary word that best completes the sentence. In some cases, you may need to change the tense or form of a verb or the number of a noun.

pariah	flaunt	misogyny	censor	beget	capitalize
bane	felony	fidelity	incite	glorify	chauvinism

1. Despite the numerous malfunctions and repairs, we maintained _____ to the idea that our invention would work correctly at the robotics fair.

2. Waka Flocka and PETA's campaign was sure to _____ a greater awareness of the amount of fur used in the fashion industry.

3. The tabloid _____ on the feud between Kanye West and 50 Cent in an effort to increase sales of the magazine.

4. Many of the scarier and more graphic scenes had to be _____ when the horror movie was shown on television.

5. A comment from a student about the poem _____ a discussion about whether the poem is about love or Nature.

6. Jack's careless work and inability to handle criticism made him the _____ of the art school.

7. The _____ of the old British Empire led to the oppression of people in many different countries.

8. The accusation of stealing lyrics became the _____ of Task1ne's musical existence, and he has had to constantly defend himself.

9. After the jury deliberated for an entire week, the computer hacker was convicted of multiple _____.

10. The documentary _____ the life of farmers while ignoring their hard work, problems with weather, and the high cost of equipment.

11. The jokes on the website were degrading toward women, and readers wondered whether the appearance of _____ was intentional.

12. Shauna likes to _____ the fact that she was accepted into Harvard by showing everyone her acceptance letter.

EXERCISE 3 / READING COMPREHENSION AND ANALYSIS

Select the best answers to the following questions based on a close and thorough reading of "Rap's Wrongs."

1. As a whole, this passage is organized by
   A. chronology.
   B. importance.
   C. point and counterpoint.
   D. topic.
   E. question and answer.

2. What is illogical about the following two sentences?

   "Many have strongly criticized the content of rap lyrics, much of which encourages drug use and violence and promotes disrespect for women. Critics point to the dangerous and illegal behaviors of some rap artists."

   A. The opinions of the critics do not represent the opinions of the author and fans of rap music, who generally believe there is nothing wrong with rap lyrics.
   B. Of the three things that rap music encourages, only "drug use" and "violence" are illegal, while "disrespect for women" is not.
   C. Having one immediately follow the other suggests that the second backs up the first, but "illegal behaviors" do not make someone write specific types of lyrics.
   D. The critics don't have a good understanding of rap music; therefore, they are unqualified to give an opinion about what they do not understand.
   E. People interpret lyrics in different ways, and many listeners of rap hear the lyrics but do not participate in "dangerous and illegal behaviors."

3. With which of the following statements would the author most likely agree?

   A. Rap music should be censored.

   B. People can be influenced by music.

   C. There are no female rappers.

   D. All rappers are materialistic.

   E. Rap music should be banned.

4. Based on the passage, which of the following is NOT a reason someone might oppose rap?

   A. It may encourage men to cheat.

   B. It may lead to materialism.

   C. It contains vulgar lyrics.

   D. It can inspire criminal behavior.

   E. It has no artistic value.

5. What would be the best alternative title for this passage?

   A. The Dangers of Rap Music

   B. Misogyny in the Hip-Hop World

   C. Living in the Inner City

   D. The Many Qualities of Rap

   E. Why Rap Should Be Listened To

EXERCISE 4 / MAKING INFERENCES

Choose the best answer.

1. Which of the following would likely NOT **incite** an argument in a basketball game?

    A. insulting the other players' skills

    B. deliberately breaking the rules

    C. encouraging someone to take a 3-point shot

    D. accusing the other team of cheating

2. Of the following, which is an INCORRECT use of the word **fidelity**?

    A. A religious man has fidelity to his god.

    B. A soldier shows fidelity to his king and country.

    C. A physics theory demonstrates fidelity to scientific principles.

    D. An honest person has fidelity and does not lie.

3. Which of following is a reason a book might be **censored**?

    A. The author insults real people by name.

    B. The author lives a lifestyle people don't support.

    C. The book contains extreme political viewpoints.

    D. The book is unpopular and isn't selling well.

4. Which of the following statements would indicate a **chauvinistic** attitude, but not a **misogynistic** one?

    A. Women should not be allowed to be pilots, even if they are trained and capable.

    B. Americans are braver and more intelligent than people in other countries are.

    C. Wives should be denied the right to divorce their husbands.

    D. Only men should be CEOs of companies and partners in law firms.

5. What can be inferred from the following statement from the passage?

    "Fans have committed crimes in an effort to gain the same types of reputations as their idols (or the personalities that the artists portray in their lyrics)."

    A. Some rappers aren't really "gangstas," but they pretend to be.

    B. All rappers deliberately inspire their fans to commit crimes.

    C. Hip-hop artists glorify the criminal nature of life in the inner city.

    D. The personas in the songs are more dangerous than the artists are.

EXERCISE 5 / ROOTS, PREFIXES, AND SUFFIXES

Answer the questions below that are designed to help you arrive at some conclusions about word families and origins.

Root: *fid*, "faith, trust"

1. Based on your knowledge of the root *fid* and how it is used in the following sentence, define the italicized word.

   He felt a great deal of *confidence* about his school's chances of winning the basketball championship.

   _____

2. Which word best fits the definition of "a signed statement that a person swears is true"?

   A. affidavit

   B. confidante

   C. infidel

   D. confidentiality

3. The prefix *mis–* means "opposing, hating." If *anthropology* is the study of people, *misanthropy* probably means

   A. the hatred of men.

   B. the opposition of human laws.

   C. the dislike of the study of people.

   D. the hatred of humanity in general.

THE ROOTS OF RAP

HIP-HOP HAS MANY elements, including fashion, art, language, attitude, and lifestyle. One of the most important parts of hip-hop culture, however, is rap. While it has now become popular and widespread, it began as a musical style unique to the inner city.

Rap was created in the Bronx, NY, in the 1970s, but it is derived from older forms of music like the songs of the African griots and Jamaican "toasting." Griots told stories through song for entertainment, as well as to keep a record of family **genealogies** and important events. These songs would then be passed down from generation to generation. Some griots were hired by wealthy **patrons**, while others worked independently. Most of the musical components of rap, however, come from Jamaican toasting. Disc jockeys ("DJs") mixed existing tracks, usually American Rhythm & Blues (R&B), on sound systems. They then added their own lyrics, energizing the audience and encouraging the people to dance.

One famous toaster and the first rap artist was Clive Campbell, a DJ who went by the name DJ Kool Herc. Originally from Jamaica, he was inspired by toasting, from which he developed a new style that was far from **conventional**. He used a technique called "breakbeat," repeating the most rhythmic parts of songs using two turntables. He played at places within the city, and on one now-famous occasion, at his sister's party in the Bronx. He then began performing at larger venues and later, added other emcees ("masters of ceremonies") who called themselves "The Herculoids."

Rap music has changed over the decades, and while it varies by artist and region, there are some common aspects. For example, when "scratching," the DJ keeps the needle in place on the turntable while moving the record back and forth. In "cutting," one recording is interrupted by another, often with a repetitive phrase. DJs also add their own lyrics that are spoken in a certain rhythm and **tempo**, incorporating the **jargon** of the streets. The language in each rap uses carefully placed syllables and accents, as well as the occasional rhyme. In many ways, it is a modern form of poetry.

The themes of rap music are **pertinent** and expose the problems faced in **impoverished** urban areas—like the Bronx. Many residents are forced to live in **atrocious** conditions in which apartments and houses are run by slumlords and not well kept. Drug use, crime, and gang violence are common. Some inner-city youth feel that social advancement is **futile** because of the widespread racism and oppression that **dominate** their daily lives. Rap music, however, brings these issues to the media's attention and empowers young people by showing that their experiences are shared.

Living in a dangerous urban area makes an artist seem more **legitimate**, proving that he or she has survived in a difficult environment and understands the problems faced on the streets. Because of this, many rappers mention the cities in which they live, and some even praise the violent crime there. In fact, there is sometimes rivalry between rappers based on location, such as the East Coast (New York) or the West Coast (Los Angeles). It is not unusual for rappers to **denigrate** and insult each other in order to gain status, regardless of popularity or record sales.

Rap will continue to develop over the decades, just as it has since the 1970s, and, more than likely, it will remain a meaningful and creative form of musical and cultural expression.

9

EXERCISE 1 / WORD LIST

Use the context in which the word is used to determine what the word probably means. Write a brief definition in the space provided.

1. **atrocious:** _____

   Many residents are forced to live in **atrocious** conditions in which apartments and houses are run by slumlords and not well kept.

2. **conventional:** _____

   Originally from Jamaica, he was inspired by toasting, from which he developed a new style that was far from **conventional**.

3. **denigrate:** _____

   It is not unusual for rappers to **denigrate** and insult each other in order to gain status...

4. **dominate:** _____

   Some inner-city youth feel that social advancement is futile because of the widespread racism and oppression that **dominate** their daily lives.

5. **futile:** _____

   Some inner-city youth feel that social advancement is **futile** because of the widespread racism and oppression that dominate their daily lives.

6. **genealogy:** _____

   Griots told stories through song for entertainment, as well as to keep a record of family **genealogies** and important events.

7. **impoverished:** _____

   The themes of rap music are pertinent and expose the problems faced in **impoverished** urban areas...

8. **jargon:** _____

   DJs also add their own lyrics that are spoken in a certain rhythm and tempo, incorporating the **jargon** of the streets.

9. **legitimate:** _____

   Living in a dangerous urban area makes an artist seem more **legitimate**, proving that he or she has survived in a difficult environment and understands the problems faced on the streets.

10. **patron:** _____

    Some griots were hired by wealthy **patrons**, while others worked independently.

11. **pertinent:** _____

    The themes of rap music are **pertinent** and expose the problems faced in impoverished urban areas...

12. **tempo:** _____

    DJs also add their own lyrics that are spoken in a certain rhythm and **tempo**, incorporating the jargon of the streets.

EXERCISE 2 / USING WORDS IN CONTEXT

Fill in the blank with the vocabulary word that best completes the sentence. In some cases, you may need to change the tense or form of a verb or the number of a noun.

| genealogy | pertinent | denigrate | jargon | dominate | impoverished |
| tempo | futile | patron | atrocious | legitimate | conventional |

1. Kanye West has frequently _____ the charts, and *The Life of Pablo* went platinum even though it was available only through streaming.

2. It is not fair to _____ a person for something he or she cannot control.

3. Coolio's "Gangsta's Paradise" may have some _____ meaning for people who can't seem to escape a life of crime and violence.

4. Since their terrible breakup, getting them to even be in the same room together without an argument is _____.

5. A lot of the _____ Eminem uses in his lyrics comes directly from the streets of Detroit where he grew up.

6. Most people did not like his writing style because it was too _____ and uninteresting.

7. People question whether her complaints about the record label are _____ because her opinions have been wrong in the past.

8. The _____, false, and personal way the magazine insulted Jay-Z angered many fans.

9. The wealthy doctor helped the _____ neighborhood he grew up in by volunteering to work in the hospital for free.

10. My sister tried to convince me that the _____ of an old Run-D.M.C. song is perfect to dance to.

11. Dr. Dre became a(n) _____ for many rap artists who were just getting started in the industry.

12. The magazine created a(n) _____ of rap musicians who had been connected with N.W.A at some time.

EXERCISE 3 / READING COMPREHENSION AND ANALYSIS

Select the best answers to the following questions based on a close and thorough reading of "The Roots of Rap."

1. The author's intention in this passage is to

   A. persuade the reader that rap is a superior form of music.

   B. correct misinformation about themes in rap.

   C. promote the music of DJ Kool Herc.

   D. provide factual information about the history of rap.

   E. condemn the poor conditions of the inner city.

2. What CANNOT be inferred about the Bronx in the 1970s based on the information in the passage?

   A. It was a poor and dangerous part of the city.

   B. There was a large Jamaican American community.

   C. Its inhabitants were subject to racism.

   D. The living conditions were terrible.

   E. It had a unique lingo, which was incorporated into rap music.

3. The "sound systems" mentioned in the second paragraph most likely refer to

   A. turntables.

   B. speakers.

   C. DJs.

   D. emcees.

   E. computers.

4. Why was DJ Kool Herc's performance at his sister's party famous?

    A. It was the first time rap music became its own musical style.

    B. There is contradictory information about what the party was for.

    C. The Herculoids performed with him for the first time.

    D. The author does not provide an explanation.

    E. There was a protest outside the apartment complex.

5. With which of these statements is the author most likely to agree?

    A. All rap music has the same rhythm.

    B. Female rap artists are overlooked and underpaid.

    C. Rap from the East Coast is better than West Coast rap.

    D. Rap will be different in ten years.

    E. The lyrics in rap are generally offensive.

EXERCISE 4 / MAKING INFERENCES

Choose the best answer.

1. You would most likely research your **genealogy** using

    A. articles about life during a particular time period.

    B. birth certificates and marriage licenses.

    C. antiques found in a relative's house.

    D. a textbook on inherited diseases.

2. If your friend were the person to **dominate** a conversation, she would NOT

    A. talk excessively.

    B. interrupt other people.

    C. sit and listen quietly.

    D. express strong opinions.

3. Which of the following people would be considered a **patron**?

    A. the CEO of a large corporation

    B. someone who is paid to write music

    C. a person who gives money to a theater program

    D. someone who collects paintings for his or her home

4. Based on the sixth paragraph, what can you infer is the "status" rap artists want to achieve?

    A. integrity

    B. reputation

    C. wealth

    D. record sales

5. One would most likely hear **jargon** in a

    A. conversation among friends.

    B. parent-teacher conference.

    C. local news broadcast.

    D. piece of classical music.

EXERCISE 5 / ROOTS, PREFIXES, AND SUFFIXES

Answer the questions below that are designed to help you arrive at some conclusions about word families and origins.

Roots: *patr*, "father"
       temp, "time"

1. A *patriot* is someone loyal to his or her _____.

2. The prefix *ex–* means "outside." Match the correct word containing *patr* or *temp* to its definition. Use a dictionary if necessary.

   _____ a person who lives outside of his or her   A. extemporaneous
   native country or fatherland   B. paternity

   _____ beat; rhythm   C. tempo

   _____ spur of the moment; unplanned   D. expatriate

   _____ fatherhood

3. Ken was a *paternal* figure for Kim, who had lost her parents when she was very young. Ken treated Kim like his

   A. child.

   B. boss.

   C. neighbor.

   D. parent.

4. Look up the word *contemporary* in a dictionary and separate it into its prefix, *con–*, root, *temp*, and suffix, *–ary*. Then, define the prefix and suffix and determine what the meaning of *contemporary* is in the following sentence:

   Joseph Saddler (Grandmaster Flash) was an early rap artist and was not a contemporary of Calvin Broadus (Snoop Dogg).

   _____

   _____

   _____

   _____

"RAPPER'S DELIGHT"

ALTHOUGH THE ROOTS of rap music extend deeply into all forms of popular American music, rap's **genesis** came from an unlikely song: "Rapper's Delight" by the Sugarhill Gang. The 1979 hit sold millions of copies in the United States and was the **catalyst** that expanded rap beyond the New York City club and party scene.

The Sugarhill Gang wasn't an existing rap **entity**. It was a group that Sylvia Robinson, the cofounder of a small, struggling label called Sugar Hill Records, pieced together. She and her husband, Joe, named the company for the Sugar Hill area of Harlem, an **elite**, wealthy African American neighborhood in New York City. In the early- to mid-1900s, Sugar Hill was a gathering place for many artists and performers. "Rapper's Delight" was the Sugar Hill label's first record.

Sylvia Robinson, known as "the mother of hip-hop," enjoyed early success in the 1950s and 1960s as a singer, songwriter, and music label executive. In 1972, she wrote a song called "Pillow Talk" and sent a demo of it to soul singer Al Green to record. Green found the lyrics too **licentious** and offensive because of his religious beliefs, so he decided not to do it. Robinson did not let Green's rejection **impede** her, however. She recorded the song herself. "Pillow Talk" became a major hit, reaching Number One on the R&B chart and restarting Robinson's solo career.

By 1979, Robinson had been hearing rap music performed live at clubs and parties for a few years. She knew that she wanted Sugar Hill Records to produce a rap album, but she had trouble finding someone willing to record a rap song. Most of the rappers who performed in clubs at the time did not want to record because they believed that **bandying** words in freestyle rapping would be **feasible** only in live performances. Robinson eventually recruited local rappers from Englewood, New Jersey, to form a group. Her new **affiliates** were Michael "Wonder Mike" Wright, Henry "Big Bank Hank" Jackson, and Guy "Master Gee" O'Brien.

In the recording studio, Robinson decided to **amalgamate** parts of the group Chic's popular song "Good Times" with portions of the incomplete "Rapper's Delight" to form a new song. The original writers objected, but they and Robinson came to an agreement, avoiding a lawsuit. This process of using parts of existing songs in new songs came to be known as "sampling." Since then, "Good Times" has become one of the most sampled songs in history. Once the Sugarhill Gang worked out the parts, they recorded the song in one take, a difficult task in itself. Drum machines were not widely used at that time, so the drummer and bass player needed to play for fifteen minutes straight with no mistakes, making the one-take recording an even greater feat.

"Rapper's Delight" was not the world's first true rap song, but it revolutionized the music industry in many ways. It brought rap to a wider audience, it was the first song to be recorded by people who considered themselves a rap group, and it was an inspiration to other artists.

EXERCISE 1 / WORD LIST

Use the context in which the word is used to determine what the word probably means. Write a brief definition in the space provided.

1. **affiliate:** _____

   Robinson eventually recruited local rappers from Englewood, New Jersey, to form a group. Her new **affiliates** were Michael "Wonder Mike" Wright, Henry "Big Bank Hank" Jackson, and Guy "Master Gee" O'Brien.

2. **amalgamate:** _____

   In the recording studio, Robinson decided to **amalgamate** parts of the group Chic's popular song "Good Times" with portions of the incomplete "Rapper's Delight" to form a new song.

3. **bandy:** _____

   Most of the rappers who performed in clubs at the time did not want to record because they believed that **bandying** words in freestyle rapping would be feasible only in live performances.

4. **catalyst:** _____

   The 1979 hit sold millions of copies in the United States and was the **catalyst** that expanded rap beyond the New York City club and party scene.

5. **elite:** _____

   She and her husband, Joe, named the company for the Sugar Hill area of Harlem, an **elite**, wealthy African American neighborhood in New York City.

6. **entity:** _____

   The Sugarhill Gang wasn't an existing rap **entity**. It was a group that Sylvia Robinson, the cofounder of a small, struggling label called Sugar Hill Records, pieced together.

7. **feasible:** _____

   Most of the rappers who performed in clubs at the time did not want to record because they believed that bandying words in freestyle rapping would be **feasible** only in live performances.

8. **genesis:** _____

   Although the roots of rap music extend deeply into all forms of popular American music, rap's **genesis** came from an unlikely song: "Rapper's Delight" by the Sugarhill Gang.

9. **impede:** _____

Robinson did not let Green's rejection **impede** her, however. She recorded the song herself.

10. **licentious:** _____

Green found the lyrics too **licentious** and offensive because of his religious beliefs, so he decided not to do it.

EXERCISE 2 / USING WORDS IN CONTEXT

Fill in the blank with the vocabulary word that best completes the sentence. In some cases, you may need to change the tense or form of a verb or the number of a noun.

affiliate	amalgamate	bandy	catalyst	elite
entity	feasible	genesis	impede	licentious

1. Before Eminem, few people thought the idea of a successful white rapper was even

   _____.

2. The siblings _____ words as they argued over whose turn it was to play the video game.

3. Sean P. Diddy Combs's clothing line was the _____ that enabled him to expand beyond music.

4. A lack of radio stations that would play hip-hop _____ the music's general acceptance.

5. Since the movie contains some _____ scenes, as well as violent ones, it has been given an R rating.

6. The corporation is headquartered in Oregon, but its New York branch has become its most successful _____.

7. Many rappers felt that music should be made by common, ordinary people, rather than by _____ musicians with classical training.

8. Scientists think that the Big Bang was the _____ of the universe, as the explosion caused matter to expand and form galaxies.

9. Public Enemy was able to _____ Chuck D's incredible lyrics and Flavor Flav's amazing style into serious social commentary.

10. We discovered that what was making howling noises in the field at night was a coyote, not the alien _____ Bob thought it was.

EXERCISE 3 / READING COMPREHENSION AND ANALYSIS

Select the best answers to the following questions based on a close and thorough reading of "Rapper's Delight."

1. Which artist did the Sugarhill Gang sample parts of a song from when recording "Rapper's Delight"?

   A. Al Green

   B. Wonder Mike

   C. Master Gee

   D. Chic

   E. Big Bank Hank

2. Before the Sugarhill Gang released "Rapper's Delight," where could people listen to rap music?

   A. only in the Sugar Hill neighborhood

   B. in New York City clubs and parties

   C. in clubs across the United States

   D. on local New York City radio stations

   E. in a few large concert halls

3. Based on information in the passage, why is the song "Pillow Talk" significant?

   A. "Pillow Talk" was the first real rap song.

   B. The song was the first recorded by the Sugarhill Gang.

   C. Al Green's part in the song made Sylvia Robinson famous.

   D. It revived Sylvia Robinson's career as a solo artist.

   E. "Pillow Talk" was frequently sampled by rap artists.

4. Which statement is the most accurate and complete paraphrase of the author's sentence: "['Rapper's Delight'] brought rap to a wider audience, it was the first song to be recorded by people who considered themselves a rap group, and it was an inspiration to other artists"?

   A. "['Rapper's Delight'] helped people understand that rap was a brand-new type of music, no one considered themselves a rap group, and other artists sampled it."

   B. "['Rapper's Delight'] was played in public areas, people who considered themselves a rap group wrote it, and its success was something other artists envied."

   C. "['Rapper's Delight'] gave rap a larger audience, it was the first song that people who considered themselves a rap group performed, and other artists saw it as something inspiring."

   D. "['Rapper's Delight'] brought rap to the public, but it was not the first song to be recorded by people who considered themselves a rap group, even though other rap artists were inspired by it."

   E. "['Rapper's Delight'] introduced people to rap music, it was the first rap song ever performed, and other artists saw it as inspiring."

5. What would be the best alternative title for this passage?

   A. The First Rap Song

   B. Live Rap Music

   C. Sylvia Robinson: R&B Star

   D. Rap's Big Break

   E. The History of the Sugarhill Gang

EXERCISE 4 / MAKING INFERENCES

Choose the best answer.

1. All of the following are examples of a **catalyst** EXCEPT

    A. a spark that starts a wildfire.

    B. a chemical that causes an explosion.

    C. a playful dog that loves the ocean.

    D. a protest march that leads to social change.

2. Which of the following best illustrates something **impeding** the process of creating an album?

    A. The lead singer quits.

    B. Other artists act as inspiration.

    C. Drum machines simplify recording a beat.

    D. All the band members write song lyrics.

3. The author would probably agree with which of the following statements?

    A. Sampling music is theft of someone else's property.

    B. "Rapper's Delight" pioneered modern rap music.

    C. The Sugarhill Gang receives too much credit for popularizing rap.

    D. The only way rap music should be experienced is live.

4. What can you infer might be a potential problem with any type of sampling?

    A. Listeners will find music featuring sampled songs boring.

    B. Songs that include sampled tracks will lack any originality.

    C. Without drum machines, sampling is a difficult process.

    D. The original artists might sue samplers for stealing their work.

5. Which of the following could best be described as **elite**?

    A. a technology researcher

    B. a computer repair technician

    C. the owner of a tech company

    D. a computer programmer

EXERCISE 5 / ROOTS, PREFIXES, AND SUFFIXES

Answer the questions below that are designed to help you arrive at some conclusions about word families and origins.

1. Briefly define **impede** in your own words. What part of speech is **impede**?

_____

_____

   A. What word is a result of changing one letter and adding *–ment* to **impede**?

      _____

      What is this new word's part of speech? What does the word mean?

      _____

   B. Divide the word into its most likely prefix and root, and define it. Use a dictionary if needed.

      _____

      _____

   C. What other words share a common root with **impede**?

      _____

RAPPER/MOVIE STAR

THIS IS A STORY all about how Will Smith's rap career went down. In West Philadelphia, PA, he was born Willard Carroll Smith, Jr., on September 25, 1968. When he was twelve years old, he met Jeffrey Townes, also known as DJ Jazzy Jeff. Though only three years older than Smith, Townes had been deejaying at parties for a while. Smith did not know it at the time, but his new affiliate, Jazzy Jeff, would be the catalyst who would play a crucial role in launching his spectacular music career.

In high school, Smith was called "Prince Charming" because he had a great deal of **charisma**. Playing off this nickname, Smith called himself "the Fresh Prince" when he rapped. The duo DJ Jazzy Jeff & The Fresh Prince teamed up with beatboxer Ready Rock C and performed in various venues across Philadelphia. In 1986, the pair released their first single, "Girls Ain't Nothing But Trouble." This song did well on the charts, spending four weeks on *Billboard*'s Top 100, and **accelerated** their music career. The following year, the duo's first full album, *Rock the House*, came out. Smith wrote fun lyrics and **refrained** from using profanity. His songs were given substantial radio play. Will Smith soon became nationally known for **buoyant**, lighthearted raps.

While many hip-hop artists focused on African Americans' struggles in the inner city, Smith wrote from his **perspective** as a suburban middle-class teenager. For example, his 1988 hit single, "Parents Just Don't Understand," includes an almost **farcical** scenario about a teenager who takes his parents' Porsche "for a little spin" and ultimately gets pulled over by the police as he attempts to impress a girl. Such amusing songs had a **catholic** appeal because young adults from a wide range of backgrounds could relate to them. Perhaps in part because their audience was made up of different types of people, DJ Jazzy Jeff &

The Fresh Prince won the Grammy Award for Best Rap Performance in 1989 for "Parents Just Don't Understand." This award was a **milestone** not only for Smith and Townes, but also for all hip-hop artists because it was the very first Grammy that honored the artistic achievement of rap music. Hip-hop's musical merits had finally been recognized.

With two popular albums out when he was only a teenager, Smith **prospered**, earning over one million dollars before he turned twenty. Unfortunately, Will spent his money too freely as he funded a **lavish** lifestyle, complete with fancy cars and a mansion with closets full of designer **apparel**. By 1990, the Fresh Prince was almost broke, and his popularity as a rapper was fading. He began looking for a new opportunity, which came in the form of the TV sitcom *The Fresh Prince of Bel-Air*. As the show title suggests, the series was based partially on Will Smith's experiences; Jeffrey Townes even appeared on multiple episodes as the Fresh Prince's friend Jazz. Like Smith's music, the television show quickly became successful. Smith then dedicated himself to acting and has starred in over twenty movies since his 1990 television debut.

Despite some movies being box-office failures, Will Smith had become a movie star, but he still released four rap albums between 1997 and 2005—performing as a solo artist. The first two solo albums, *Big Willie Style* and *Willennium*, were multi-platinum albums that sold millions of copies in the US; however, his last two albums could not replicate or even come close to that success. The Fresh Prince may not be so fresh anymore, but he certainly demonstrated that hip-hop artists can **evolve** and expand beyond the idea that all rappers are thugs, gang members, or drug dealers; Smith still appeals to a broad range of people.

EXERCISE 1 / WORD LIST

Use the context in which the word is used to determine what the word probably means. Write a brief definition in the space provided.

1. **accelerate:** _____

   This song did well on the charts, spending four weeks on *Billboard's* Top 100, and **accelerated** their music career.

2. **apparel:** _____

   Unfortunately, Will spent his money too freely as he funded a lavish lifestyle, complete with fancy cars and a mansion with closets full of designer **apparel**.

3. **buoyant:** _____

   Smith wrote fun lyrics and refrained from using profanity.…Will Smith soon became nationally known for **buoyant**, lighthearted raps.

4. **catholic:** _____

   Such amusing songs had a **catholic** appeal because young adults from a wide range of backgrounds could relate to them.

5. **charisma:** _____

   In high school, Smith was called "Prince Charming" because he had a great deal of **charisma**.

6. **evolve:** _____

   The Fresh Prince may not be so fresh anymore, but he certainly demonstrated that hip-hop artists can **evolve** and expand beyond the idea that all rappers are thugs, gang members, or drug dealers…

7. **farcical:** _____

   …his 1988 hit single, "Parents Just Don't Understand," includes an almost **farcical** scenario about a teenager who takes his parents' Porsche "for a little spin" and ultimately gets pulled over by the police as he attempts to impress a girl.

8. **lavish:** _____

   Unfortunately, Will spent his money too freely as he funded a **lavish** lifestyle, complete with fancy cars and a mansion with closets full of designer apparel.

9. **milestone:** _____

This award was a **milestone** not only for Smith and Townes, but also for all hip-hop artists because it was the very first Grammy that honored the artistic achievement of rap music.

10. **perspective:** _____

While many hip-hop artists focused on African Americans' struggles in the inner city, Smith wrote from his **perspective** as a suburban middle-class teenager.

11. **prosper:** _____

With two popular albums out when he was only a teenager, Smith **prospered**, earning over one million dollars before he turned twenty.

12. **refrain:** _____

Smith wrote fun lyrics and **refrained** from using profanity. His songs were given substantial radio play. Will Smith soon became nationally known for buoyant, lighthearted raps.

EXERCISE 2 / USING WORDS IN CONTEXT

Fill in the blank with the vocabulary word that best completes the sentence. In some cases, you may need to change the tense or form of a verb or the number of a noun.

| evolve | catholic | farcical | prosper | apparel | accelerate |
| buoyant | lavish | perspective | charisma | milestone | refrain |

1. After he spent a few years as a backup singer for Kanye West, John Legend's _____ and talent was clear, and he became a star on his own.

2. Michael Jackson's *Thriller* album has reached a(n) _____ that other artists aim for; it has sold over 65,000,000 copies, more than any other record in history.

3. A clothing designer, who had generally been known for making women's _____, started making children's backpacks last year.

4. Surprisingly, offensive lyrics can _____ someone's career, rather than slow it down.

5. Snow, rain, and then an ice storm caused the camping trip to _____ from a simple outing to a complete disaster.

6. Tupac's poems offer different _____ about love than many of his songs do.

7. The audience thought it seemed _____ for the zombie to stand up and begin singing.

8. We hired a clown to appear at the birthday party; she was funny, friendly, _____, and made all the kids happy.

9. Mr. Browne was an unusual man with _____ musical tastes; he enjoyed both Beethoven and Biggie Smalls.

10. The singer's posse didn't really like her; they stayed around just for the _____ parties, food, and entertainment.

11. No one in the singing group _____, so Mike quit and tried to become a solo artist.

12. There were signs all over the zoo instructing people to _____ from feeding the animals.

EXERCISE 3 / READING COMPREHENSION AND ANALYSIS

Select the best answers to the following questions based on a close and thorough reading of "Rapper/Movie Star."

1. According to the passage, Smith won a Grammy for

   A. "Girls Ain't Nothing But Trouble."

   B. "Parents Just Don't Understand."

   C. *The Fresh Prince of Bel-Air.*

   D. *Big Willie Style.*

   E. *Willennium.*

2. The author writes, "The Fresh Prince may not be so fresh anymore, but he certainly demonstrated that hip-hop artists can evolve and expand beyond the idea that all rappers are thugs, gang members, or drug dealers; Smith still appeals to a broad range of people." What is the best explanation of the second use of the word *fresh*?

   A. It is intended to show that Smith's rapping is still important.

   B. It explains how the author really feels about Smith's career.

   C. It is saying that Smith is not as popular as he once was.

   D. The author is trying to criticize Smith's becoming a movie star.

   E. The author is complaining that Smith has no appeal to criminals.

3. Which of the following is the most accurate summary of "Like Smith's music, the television show [*The Fresh Prince*] quickly became successful. Smith then dedicated himself to acting and has starred in over twenty movies since his 1990 television debut"?

   A. *The Fresh Prince* was a huge success, and Smith has acted in over twenty movies since then.

   B. After starring in more than twenty movies since 1990, Smith also had great success in his TV show and has dedicated himself to acting.

   C. Since his debut on TV, Smith has become a movie star and acted in over twenty successful movies since 1990.

   D. Once he became a TV actor in *The Fresh Prince*, Smith became a movie actor in more than twenty movies after dedicating himself to his job.

   E. Since starring in the popular *Fresh Prince* series in 1990, Smith has worked hard to become a successful actor, starring in more than twenty movies.

4. How does the author arrange the facts of this passage?

   A. opposing views

   B. most important to least

   C. point-counterpoint

   D. time order

   E. least important to most

5. According to the passage, what was the importance of the Grammy Award?

   A. It helped make Smith a rap star.

   B. It was the first Grammy honoring rap.

   C. Both Smith and Townes were honored.

   D. Rap now was able to be featured on TV.

   E. The award gave Smith the chance to act.

EXERCISE 4 / MAKING INFERENCES

Choose the best answer.

1. What is the most likely reason for the author's putting quotation marks around "for a little spin" in Paragraph 3?

   A. There was an accident, which is why he "gets pulled over."

   B. Because the story is "farcical," it never really happened.

   C. They are lyrics in "Parents Just Don't Understand."

   D. The words mean that Smith wanted to "impress a girl."

2. Which could best be described as a **milestone**?

   A. your first day in kindergarten

   B. a fast-food breakfast

   C. entering a race but losing

   D. getting a B+ in biology class

3. Which is the best example of **refraining** from doing something?

   A. winning a geography contest

   B. cheating on an English exam

   C. not fighting after being insulted

   D. not caring about sports at all

4. Which is the most logical inference you can make about Will Smith after reading the passage?

   A. He is prouder of his movies than he is of his music.

   B. He was responsible for rap's general acceptance.

   C. He disliked rap, which is the reason he started acting.

   D. His success on the TV show had nothing to do with rap.

5. Which statement indicates something that **evolved**?

   A. I have always had a special preference for football, but I like all different types of sports, too.

   B. The idea of getting up at five-thirty in the morning every day to go to a job I dislike is just awful.

   C. The shows I watched on TV last year are the exact same ones that I like watching this year.

   D. I used to hate vegetables, but ever since I had them properly made, I've learned to love them.

EXERCISE 5 / ROOTS, PREFIXES, AND SUFFIXES

Answer the questions below that are designed to help you arrive at some conclusions about word families and origins.

1. A. The word **evolve** contains the root *volv*. List some other words that contain the *volv* root.

    _____

    B. **Evolve** is a verb. What is the noun form of this verb?

    _____

    C. *Revolution* (from the Latin root *volut*, "to turn") can mean "trip around." Earth makes one revolution around the sun every 365 days. What is another meaning of *revolution*?

    _____

2. The Latin root *spect* means "to see." How would you define the word **perspective**?

    _____

3. Based on the following sentence and your knowledge of the *volut* root, what does the word *convoluted* mean?

    It was hard to make sense of Dean's *convoluted* story.

    A. loud; offensive

    B. twisted; mixed up

    C. beautiful; interesting; thrilling

    D. intimidating; silly; illogical

4. **Prosper** comes from the prefix *pro–* and the Latin root *sper*, which means "hope." Another word from the same root is *despair*, which means "deep sadness." Explain how *despair* might come from the *sper* root.

    _____

HIP-HOP CULTURE

YOU'VE PROBABLY NOTICED the guy on the street corner with his pants hanging low, walking with an odd **gait**. You may have also seen his girlfriend in baggy athletic clothing with hoop earrings so big you could wear them around your waist. If someone were a grumpy old **ogre** with **superficial** views, he might brush the two of them off with a "kids'-clothes-these-days" kind of attitude. The biggest problem is that what he considers a fad has been around for decades. Fashion, however, is just a small part of hip-hop culture, which includes not only music, but also other forms of expression like art and dance.

The spray-painted graffiti in back alleys is not the work of troublemakers with too much time on their hands. Instead, it is a form of art with special meaning. Some of it falls into the category of "tagging" in which artists or crews **deface** public places with symbols or false names to mark their territories. Others may use familiar logos, cartoons, or images to make statements, ranging from intellectual to **obscene**. Daring graffiti artists can also become famous for painting in dangerous places. They dangle over the sides of buildings and climb over barbed-wire fences. Sometimes, they have to outrun guard dogs. This behavior **glamorizes** the criminal image that they desire. In the 1970s, there was so much graffiti on the subway trains that New York City developed a special program to remove the paint from the cars. The destruction of public property is illegal, but some talented artists were hired to create murals or pieces for art galleries. One famous graffiti artist was Jean-Michel Basquiat, whose **vivid**, imaginative work has appeared in many museums, including New York's Museum of Modern Art. One of his paintings even sold for $110 million dollars!

In addition to graffiti art, breakdancing is often associated with hip-hop culture. Like rap music, it has historical roots. It was inspired by older dances like the cakewalk, lindy-hop, and Charleston, which were in vogue in the late 19th and early 20th centuries. In breakdancing, energetic, **boisterous** crowds form a circle, and one person enters the center to demonstrate his or her best moves. Most of the dances require special athletic skill, and dancers sometimes perform amazing acrobatics like headstands and backflips. The winner is the person the audience agrees is the best. While breakdancing may seem like just a fun activity, it may have started as a way to discourage violence between gangs by having them compete in dancing instead.

There is also a distinct fashion associated with hip-hop, and baggy, low-hanging pants are just one example. People try to suggest status and wealth by wearing expensive clothes with **ostentatious** displays of designer logos, as well as heavy gold or platinum chains and diamonds. Most of the clothing, including hoodies and T-shirts, is oversized, and sociologists explain this in many ways. The fit may be based on a form of traditional African clothing made from a single square piece of fabric to create a loose-fitting garment. It could also have been inspired by ill-fitting clothes handed down from relatives or the standard uniforms inmates wear that are often too large. The best explanation, however, is that the style is simply a refusal to **conform** to accepted fashion standards.

Regardless of what your opinion might be on hip-hop culture, it is more than just a passing trend and far more complex than you'd previously assumed.

EXERCISE 1 / WORD LIST

Use the context in which the word is used to determine what the word probably means. Write a brief definition in the space provided.

1. **boisterous:** _____

   In breakdancing, energetic, **boisterous** crowds form a circle, and one person enters the center to demonstrate his or her best moves.

2. **conform:** _____

   The best explanation, however, is that the style is simply a refusal to **conform** to accepted fashion standards.

3. **deface:** _____

   Some of it falls into the category of "tagging" in which artists or crews **deface** public places with symbols or false names to mark their territories.

4. **gait:** _____

   You've probably noticed the guy on the street corner with his pants hanging low, walking with an odd **gait**.

5. **glamorize:** _____

   Daring graffiti artists can also become famous for painting in dangerous places. They dangle over the sides of buildings and climb over barbed-wire fences. Sometimes, they have to outrun guard dogs. This behavior **glamorizes** the criminal image that they desire.

6. **obscene:** _____

   Others may use familiar logos, cartoons, or images to make statements, ranging from intellectual to **obscene**.

7. **ogre:** _____

   If someone were a grumpy old **ogre** with superficial views, he might brush the two of them off with a "kids'-clothes-these-days" kind of attitude.

8. **ostentatious:** _____

   People try to suggest status and wealth by wearing expensive clothes with **ostentatious** displays of designer logos, as well as heavy gold or platinum chains and diamonds.

9. **superficial:** _____

   If someone were a grumpy old ogre with **superficial** views, he might brush the two of them off with a "kids'-clothes-these-days" kind of attitude.

10. **vivid:** _____

    One famous graffiti artist was Jean-Michel Basquiat, whose **vivid**, imaginative work has appeared in many museums, including New York's Museum of Modern Art.

EXERCISE 2 / USING WORDS IN CONTEXT

Fill in the blank with the vocabulary word that best completes the sentence. In some cases, you may need to change the tense or form of a verb or the number of a noun.

boisterous	conform	vivid	deface	ostentatious
superficial	gait	ogre	obscene	glamorize

1. The Tennessee Walking Horse has a unique _____, picking its legs up high and doing a "running-walk."

2. Many rap artists display their wealth by driving _____ cars, just like 50 Cent drives a Ferrari F430.

3. Tourists were no longer allowed in the tomb after someone _____ the hieroglyphics on the walls of the inner chamber.

4. That new song demonstrates such a(n) _____ understanding of what rap sounds like that no real rap artist could have written it.

5. His crude poem may seem _____ until you realize it's a metaphor for dealing with grief and feeling powerless.

6. The newspaper did not print any opinion articles that did not _____ to their closed-minded beliefs.

7. To get away from the crowded and _____ city, Jay-Z took a vacation to a quiet island.

8. Some people criticize hip-hop for _____ drug use and gang violence, but I don't think they understand the harsh reality and serious message behind it.

9. The dress Beyoncé wore to the Emmys had such bright, _____ colors that she captured the attention of all the photographers.

10. The _____ downstairs accused me of playing my music too loud last night, but I wasn't even home.

EXERCISE 3 / READING COMPREHENSION AND ANALYSIS

Select the best answers to the following questions based on a close and thorough reading of "Hip-Hop Culture."

1. The writer's tone in the first paragraph can best be described as

    A. snobbish.

    B. humorous.

    C. argumentative.

    D. concerned.

    E. indifferent.

2. The reference to Jean-Michel Basquiat is intended to

    A. make a connection between graffiti art and hip-hop.

    B. compare graffiti art to modern art in museums.

    C. explain how rap music inspires inner-city artists.

    D. show some common themes expressed in graffiti.

    E. support the previous statement about talented artists.

3. Which sentence in Paragraph 2 could be omitted without weakening the point?

    A. "Some of it falls into the category of 'tagging' in which artists or crews deface public places with symbols or false names to mark their territories."

    B. "Daring graffiti artists can also become famous for painting in dangerous places."

    C. "This behavior glamorizes the criminal image that they desire."

    D. "In the 1970s, there was so much graffiti on the subway trains that New York City developed a special program to remove the paint from the cars."

    E. "The destruction of public property is illegal, but some talented artists were hired to create murals or pieces for art galleries."

4. What information would make the author's main point of Paragraph 3 invalid?

   A. Breakdancing competitions often cause gang fights.

   B. Some breakdancing groups have appeared on television.

   C. The Jitterbug, an older dance, was a major influence on breakdancing.

   D. Breakdancing is now popular in other countries.

   E. People who breakdance are very athletic.

5. Which of the following elements of hip-hop is NOT mentioned in the passage?

   A. pants that are worn low

   B. athletic clothing

   C. large jewelry

   D. brand-name clothing

   E. oversized jerseys

EXERCISE 4 / MAKING INFERENCES

Choose the best answer.

1. You would most likely find a **boisterous** crowd

   A. in a coffee shop.

   B. at a football game.

   C. in a library.

   D. at a birthday party.

2. Based on the passage, someone with a " 'kids'-clothes-these-days' kind of attitude" believes which of the following?

   A. People who embrace hip-hop culture are criminals.

   B. Hip-hop is a new trend that will soon be over.

   C. Only the wealthy can afford brand-name clothing.

   D. Kids have no respect for their elders.

3. If someone were writing a screenplay and wanted to **glamorize** life as a doctor, the doctor would probably NOT

    A. be famous for developing a new cure.

    B. take time off whenever she wants.

    C. never make mistakes in judgment.

    D. work long hours and leave exhausted.

4. A person trying to **conform** and fit into a group would likely

    A. use specific slang words.

    B. move to a different location.

    C. wear a unique style of clothing.

    D. play a rare, 18th-century instrument.

5. Which of the following would NOT have **vivid** colors?

    A. flowers at a botanical garden

    B. photographs from the 1900s

    C. the feathers of a peacock

    D. a sunset in the mountains

EXERCISE 5 / ROOTS, PREFIXES, AND SUFFIXES

Answer the questions below that are designed to help you arrive at some conclusions about word families and origins.

Roots: *viv*, "alive"

　　　　form, "shape, form," "rule"

1. Based on the definitions provided and the meanings of *viv* and *form*, complete each word.

    to bring back to life: ___ ___ *viv* ___

    to bring back into shape: ___ ___ *form*

    a group of symbols showing a fact: *form* ___ ___ ___

    a plan, arrangement, or makeup of something: *form* ___ ___

    to stay alive; to live: ___ ___ ___ *viv* ___

    producing a strong impression on the senses: *viv* ___ ___

2. The suffix *–ous* means "full of." When might Ari seem to be the most *vivacious*?

    A. when she is studying quietly in the library
    B. when she is talking and laughing at a party

3. A. The prefix *con–* means "together with."

    Sean remembered the *convivial* behavior of the people at the wedding.

    Based on the sample sentence, the word *convivial* probably means

    A. rushed.

    B. lifeless.

    C. crowded.

    D. friendly.

    B. Based on your knowledge of the *viv* root, how do we get this meaning for *convivial*? Look up the definition of *convivial* in the dictionary and compare the definition to the way it's defined through root and prefix. How are they alike or dissimilar?

    _____

    _____

    _____

    _____

    _____

    _____

4. Using your knowledge of the root *form* and the meanings of the prefixes that follow, fill in the blank to create a word that completes the sentence.

    de– = "down," "away"
    mal– = "bad," "wrong"

    Erika had to have surgery on her _____ed (wrongly shaped) kidney.

    Acid rain threatened to _____ (take the shape away) the face of the statue.

CHUCK D AND FLAV

ARGUABLY ONE OF the most influential hip-hop groups of all time, Public Enemy made quite an impact in the late 1980s. Their raps were hard-hitting and political. They often caused **controversy** by urging black people to rebel against the existing social power structure. Calling themselves "CNN for black culture," Public Enemy rapped about African Americans' struggles, such as racism and police **bias** and brutality, that mainstream media often ignored.

Public Enemy formed in 1982 at Adelphi University, where Carl Ridenhour, rapping under stage name Chuck D, hosted a radio show with record producer Hank Shocklee. Ridenhour recorded the song "Public Enemy No. 1," which gained the attention of Rick Rubin from Def Jam Records. Chuck D signed a record deal and soon formed a crew with DJ Terminator X (Norman Rogers), Professor Griff (Richard Griffin), and Flavor Flav (William Drayton). Their first album, *Yo! Bum Rush the Show*, was not very successful, though critics recognized the group as elite, talented hip-hop artists. With their second album, *It Takes a Nation of Millions to Hold Us Back*, Public Enemy became a **formidable** force for social change.

Inspired by the Black Panthers, Public Enemy preached black power and called for the **abolition** of what they felt was a form of white supremacy that held minorities down. In his raps, Chuck D's lyrics sharply condemned racial injustice and urged African Americans to unite and fight for social change. Not only did the group pay **homage** to the Black Power movement of the 1960s through their songs, but they also honored black activists with their style. Public Enemy often posed with their fists raised in the black power salute. Their dancers and bodyguards, called the Security of the First World (S1W), performed drills with fake guns while dressed in military jackets and berets.

The rappers, on the other hand, celebrated African American urban culture by wearing dark street clothes, with one **noteworthy** exception—Flavor Flav. Flavor Flav wore flashy outfits, oversized sunglasses, and a clock around his neck. He looked very much like a **caricature** of people who wore stopwatches during the mid-1980s. This out-of-place attire suited Flavor Flav because he was the group's hype man. He cracked jokes and got the crowd **exhilarated** enough to clap or rap along with the music at concerts. The **hilarity** of Flavor Flav, who later became a Reality TV star, balanced the harsher militant vibe of the rest of the group's lyrics.

The group's dynamic blend of sounds and poetic verses about social justice raised rap music to a new level. When hip-hop had first been produced, many music critics lacked the **foresight** to see how important the genre would become. Instead, they believed that rap was merely a fad. Public Enemy proved them wrong. The group continued to gain popularity with their **anthem** "Fight the Power." Spike Lee featured it in his amazing movie *Do the Right Thing*, which emphasized the racial tensions within American cities. In 1990, their album *Fear of a Black Planet* made it on to *Billboard's* Top Ten chart. They inspired many hip-hop artists to embrace their African roots and spread important messages. Thanks to Public Enemy, rap became an art form through which oppressed minorities could **advocate** social and political change. Hip-hop had finally evolved into a form of mainstream popular music that could carry a message. Public Enemy's influence on music is unquestionable.

EXERCISE 1 / WORD LIST

Use the context in which the word is used to determine what the word probably means. Write a brief definition in the space provided.

1. **abolition:** _____

   Public Enemy...called for the **abolition** of what they felt was a form of white supremacy that held minorities down....Chuck D's lyrics sharply condemned racial injustice and urged African Americans to unite and fight for social change.

2. **advocate:** _____

   Thanks to Public Enemy, rap became an art form through which oppressed minorities could **advocate** social and political change.

3. **anthem:** _____

   The group continued to gain popularity with their **anthem** "Fight the Power." Spike Lee featured it in his amazing movie *Do the Right Thing*, which emphasized the racial tensions within American cities.

4. **bias:** _____

   Calling themselves "CNN for black culture," Public Enemy rapped about African Americans' struggles, such as racism and police **bias** and brutality, that mainstream media often ignored.

5. **caricature:** _____

   Flavor Flav wore flashy outfits, oversized sunglasses, and a clock around his neck. He looked very much like a **caricature** of people who wore stopwatches during the mid-1980s.

6. **controversy:** _____

   Their raps were hard-hitting and political. They often caused **controversy** by urging black people to rebel against the existing social power structure.

7. **exhilarated:** _____

   This out-of-place attire suited Flavor Flav because he was the group's hype man. He cracked jokes and got the crowd **exhilarated** enough to clap or rap along with the music at concerts.

8. **foresight:** _____

   When hip-hop had first been produced, many music critics lacked the **foresight** to see how important the genre would become. Instead, they believed that rap was merely a fad.

9. **formidable:** _____

   With their second album, *It Takes a Nation of Millions to Hold Us Back*, Public Enemy became a **formidable** force for social change.

10. **hilarity:** _____

    He cracked jokes and got the crowd exhilarated enough to clap or rap along with the music at concerts. The **hilarity** of Flavor Flav…balanced the harsher militant vibe of the rest of the group's lyrics.

11. **homage:** _____

    Not only did the group pay **homage** to the Black Power movement of the 1960s through their songs, but they also honored black activists with their style. Public Enemy often posed with their fists raised in the black power salute.

12. **noteworthy:** _____

    The rappers…celebrated African American urban culture by wearing dark street clothes, with one **noteworthy** exception—Flavor Flav. Flavor Flav wore flashy outfits, oversized sunglasses, and a clock around his neck.

EXERCISE 2 / USING WORDS IN CONTEXT

Fill in the blank with the vocabulary word that best completes the sentence. In some cases, you may need to change the tense or form of a verb or the number of a noun.

foresight	homage	caricature	noteworthy	formidable	bias
abolition	anthem	advocate	controversy	exhilarated	hilarity

1. All the children were enjoying the _____ of the food fight, but their parents were upset by the mess.

2. My friends were _____ at being able to get six front-row seats for next month's Beyoncé concert.

3. Juan was too young to go see Snoop by himself, so his dad took him to the show; Mr. Hopkins said he was glad he had the _____ to bring earplugs, though.

4. Many songs convey messages in their lyrics, but Public Enemy's _____ are particularly strong and forceful.

5. One of the most _____ accomplishments of the Internet is that you can find almost any information in a few seconds.

6. Many rappers sound as if they are _____ violence and drugs, but most of them are only trying to create some hype about themselves.

7. Most people think that the male lion is the most _____ force in the African jungle, but, in actuality, the female does most of the hunting and killing.

8. I saw a(n) _____ of 50 Cent's album *Before I Self Destruct* that was so funny I copied it and hung it on my wall.

9. There was a huge _____ about Ice-T's song "Cop Killer," but a few years later, he started playing a New York police detective on TV.

10. Many citizens feel that the _____ of bad news would make life more enjoyable, but people need to be informed, even about things that they dislike.

11. After the death of ODB, an original member of Wu-Tang Clan, the group paid _____ to him by having his mother and son sing a few of his songs during concerts.

12. It really is disgusting that so many rap songs have a huge negative _____ against women because they do not deserve to be treated that way.

EXERCISE 3 / READING COMPREHENSION AND ANALYSIS

Select the best answers to the following questions based on a close and thorough reading of "Chuck D and Flav."

1. How has the author developed the idea of the importance of Public Enemy?

    A. The author explains how many millions of records PE sold.

    B. The author emphasizes PE's message of social justice.

    C. The author discusses Flavor Flav's contributions to PE.

    D. The author claims that PE influenced many other artists.

    E. The author explains how PE's words and sounds fit together.

2. Who were the original members of Public Enemy?

    A. Ridenhour, Rogers, Drayton, Griffin

    B. Drayton, Rogers, Shocklee, Ridenhour

    C. Griffin, Drayton, Ridenhour, Chuck D

    D. Rubin, Ridenhour, Drayton, Rogers

    E. Terminator X, Hank, Flav, Chuck D

3. All these statements about the Security of the First World are false EXCEPT

 A. they dressed exactly like the Black Panthers.

 B. they acted as the group's fans on stage.

 C. they posed with their fists in the air.

 D. they were dancers, as well as bodyguards.

 E. they shot guns during some of the shows.

4. Which statement best describes how the third paragraph fits into the structure of the entire passage?

 A. It explains how Public Enemy honored the Black Panthers.

 B. It explains the role that the Security of the First World played in PE.

 C. It adds more information about the message PE wanted to convey.

 D. It explains that PE used dancers and style to get the message across.

 E. It describes how Chuck D wanted his audience to unite during the songs.

5. Based on information in the passage, which comment would the author most likely DISAGREE with?

 A. PE never would have succeeded without Chuck D and Flavor Flav.

 B. Social problems and injustice are valid topics for rap groups to cover.

 C. Before PE, no rap group had explored social problems or prejudice.

 D. Most music critics didn't understand that rap could be a powerful force.

 E. PE's "Fight the Power" was the best thing about Spike Lee's film.

EXERCISE 4 / MAKING INFERENCES

Choose the best answer.

1. All the following phony newspaper headlines could be classified as **noteworthy** EXCEPT

    A. Inmates Complain About Prison Breakfast.

    B. Army Man Defuses NYC Subway Bomb.

    C. Longest War in US History Finally Over.

    D. Life on Earth-like Planet Discovered.

2. What made Chuck D and Flavor Flav the focus of Public Enemy?

    A. Chuck D formed the group; Flav became a TV star.

    B. Flav dressed like a criminal; Chuck D wrote the lyrics.

    C. Chuck D created the message; Flav provided the excitement.

    D. Flav formed the group; Chuck D rapped "Fight the Power."

3. When someone **advocates** for a cause, he or she

    A. discusses it with other people.

    B. hires people to support it.

    C. donates money in order to help it.

    D. thinks about it all the time.

4. Which phrase shows the writer of the passage expressing an opinion?

    A. "celebrated African American urban culture"

    B. "the harsher militant vibe"

    C. "proved them wrong"

    D. "his amazing movie"

5. If you were **exhilarated** by a song, you would probably say something like,

    A. "That is the worst thing I've ever heard!"

    B. "I'd really like to meet the person who wrote that."

    C. "I've never heard anything that great before."

    D. "It's not a bad song at all, not amazing, but decent."

EXERCISE 5 / ROOTS, PREFIXES, AND SUFFIXES

Answer the questions below that are designed to help you arrive at some conclusions about word families and origins.

1. The prefix *re–* means "back."
   The Latin root *vers/vert* means "turn."
   The Latin root *voc/vok* means "call."

   A. What word means "to turn back"?

   _____

   B. What word means "to call back"?

   _____

2. The root *annu* means "year." Based on your knowledge of the *vers* root, an *anniversary* is

   _____

3. Complete the words by filling in the blank with the root that matches the definition. You may need to add a letter to the root to form the word.

   e _____ = to call to mind

   _____ atile = able to do many different things

   con _____ = to turn something into a different form

4. The following are different forms of the words in Question 3. For each word, use a dictionary or other source to find the part of speech and definition.

   evocation = _____

   versatility = _____

   conversion = _____

THE BEASTIES

IN THE EARLY '80s, the Beastie Boys broke into the music world with a unique and **radical** style. Drawing from a hardcore punk background, they incorporated an exciting amalgamation of sampling and instrumentation into their music that continued to evolve over the years. Combined with their wild behavior both onstage and off, their songs were unforgettable and made an important contribution to hip-hop.

The Beastie Boys consisted of Michael Diamond ("Mike D"), Adam Yauch ("MCA"), and Adam Horovitz ("Ad-Rock"). The band started as a joke—just a bunch of boisterous teenagers trying to be as **obnoxious** as possible through their loud music, vulgar lyrics, and crazy behavior. Their first recorded song, "Polly Wog Stew," was **auditory** chaos, featuring components of punk like harsh screaming, guitars so loud that they **distorted** the overall sound, and extremely rapid drumming. However, the band transitioned into hip-hop when the genre started to become popular. Their second song, "Cooky Puss," contained sampling and scratching, both of which are elements of hip-hop. Despite the change in musical style, one thing remained consistent: The Beastie Boys had a **flagrant** disregard for social and musical conventions and would do almost anything to entertain their fans.

The Beasties began to gain more publicity when they performed in Madonna's Virgin Tour and Run-D.M.C.'s Raising Hell Tour. While Madonna's fans were **aghast** at the group's obscene performance and found it **repulsive**, Run-D.M.C.'s audience had the opposite response. Initially, the fans felt as though the Beastie Boys, an all-white group, stole music that was the domain of black hip-hop artists. Nevertheless, as the group **cavorted** around the stage, the audience was won over by their energy and talent.

The Beastie Boys were later signed to Def Jam Recordings, whose focus was hip-hop. The group released their first full-length album, *Licensed to Ill*, in 1986. It was an instant success, becoming the first rap album to reach Number One on the *Billboard* 200 chart. The Beasties, though, did not want to limit themselves to traditional hip-hop. When they began to experiment with new sounds, Def Jam was reluctant to release their next album, *Paul's Boutique*. The band left and signed with Capitol Records.

Over time, the group's music underwent several transformations, and their immature antics began to **abate**. They started to incorporate more political themes into their music. For example, Yauch, a Buddhist, organized The Tibetan Freedom Concert in 1996 to support the cause for Tibetan independence. The group also planned a post-9/11 benefit concert and protested the Iraq War through a song called "In a World Gone Mad" (2003). Reviews of the song were mixed, but the Beasties showed their ability to adapt to a new era.

In 1999, the Beastie Boys were **nominated** for two Grammys. Their album *Hello Nasty* won for Best Alternative Music Album, and one of their most popular songs, "Intergalactic," won for Best Rap Performance by a Duo or Group. The height of the group's success occurred in 2012 when they were inducted into the Rock & Roll Hall of Fame. Sadly, Yauch, who was battling cancer, was too ill to attend the ceremony and died several weeks later. The remaining members agreed they would never again perform under the name "Beastie Boys" out of respect for their friend.

The Beastie Boys had a lengthy career, and their music is enduring. Even decades later, their songs continue to be as popular as they were years ago. Their success is largely due to their originality and a style that changed with the times.

Who would have thought that three **impertinent** kids from New York City would have made such an impact on hip-hop?

EXERCISE 1 / WORD LIST

Use the context in which the word is used to determine what the word probably means. Write a brief definition in the space provided.

1. **abate:** _____

    Over time, the group's music underwent several transformations, and their immature antics began to **abate**. They started to incorporate more political themes into their music.

2. **aghast:** _____

    While Madonna's fans were **aghast** at the group's obscene performance and found it repulsive, Run-D.M.C.'s audience had the opposite response.

3. **auditory:** _____

    Their first recorded song, "Polly Wog Stew," was **auditory** chaos, featuring components of punk like harsh screaming, guitars so loud that they distorted the overall sound, and extremely rapid drumming.

4. **cavort:** _____

    Nevertheless, as the group **cavorted** around the stage, the audience was won over by their energy and talent.

5. **distort:** _____

    Their first recorded song, "Polly Wog Stew," was auditory chaos, featuring components of punk like harsh screaming, guitars so loud that they **distorted** the overall sound, and extremely rapid drumming.

6. **flagrant:** _____

    Despite the change in musical style, one thing remained consistent: The Beastie Boys had a **flagrant** disregard for social and musical conventions and would do almost anything to entertain their fans.

7. **impertinent:** _____

    Who would have thought that three **impertinent** kids from New York City would have made such an impact on hip-hop?

8. **nominate:** _____

In 1999, the Beastie Boys were **nominated** for two Grammys. Their album *Hello Nasty* won for Best Alternative Music Album, and one of their most popular songs, "Intergalactic," won for Best Rap Performance by a Duo or Group.

9. **obnoxious:** _____

The band started as a joke—just a bunch of boisterous teenagers trying to be as **obnoxious** as possible through their loud music, vulgar lyrics, and crazy behavior.

10. **radical:** _____

In the early '80s, the Beastie Boys broke into the music world with a unique and **radical** style. Drawing from a hardcore punk background, they incorporated an exciting amalgamation of sampling and instrumentation into their music that continued to evolve over the years.

11. **repulsive:** _____

While Madonna's fans were aghast at the group's obscene performance and found it **repulsive**, Run-D.M.C.'s audience had the opposite response.

EXERCISE 2 / USING WORDS IN CONTEXT

Fill in the blank with the vocabulary word that best completes the sentence. In some cases, you may need to change the tense or form of a verb or the number of a noun.

repulsive	radical	abate	distort	nominate	impertinent
aghast	cavort	flagrant	auditory	obnoxious	

1. Rick Ross made a(n) _____ display of his huge ego when he wore a pendant of his own face on a necklace.

2. The only _____ organ in the body, the ear, is responsible for both hearing and balance.

3. My aunt's overcooked bean casserole looked so _____ that I didn't want to try it.

4. Kanye West was rude and _____ when he interrupted Taylor Swift's acceptance speech.

5. Although the murders of Tupac Shakur and Biggie Smalls have not yet been solved, the conspiracy theories have gradually _____ over time.

6. Many artists, like Picasso, _____ the human figure in their paintings in creative ways.

7. Even though Olivia didn't win the election for class president, she was still glad that she was _____.

8. The children happily _____ around the playground when they were let out for recess early.

9. People were _____ when Nicki Minaj ridiculed religion in a performance of "Roman Holiday."

10. They made so many _____ changes to the computer program that users were confused and didn't know how to use it.

11. Although the dog's loud, yappy bark was _____, she was sweet and deeply loved by her owners.

EXERCISE 3 / READING COMPREHENSION AND ANALYSIS

Select the best answers to the following questions based on a close and thorough reading of "The Beasties."

1. Overall, what is the author's tone in this passage?

   A. awestruck

   B. inspirational

   C. critical

   D. informative

   E. defensive

2. The writer wants to add the following sentence to the passage. Choose the best paragraph in which to place it.

   "The Beastie Boys' first gig was at a party for Yauch's 17th birthday."

   A. Paragraph 1

   B. Paragraph 2

   C. Paragraph 4

   D. Paragraph 5

   E. Paragraph 6

3. Early in their career, what techniques or musical elements of hip-hop did the Beastie Boys incorporate into their music?

   A. harsh screaming

   B. breakbeat

   C. political themes

   D. sampling and scratching

   E. heavily distorted guitar sounds

4. Which of the following facts is INCORRECT, according to the passage?

   A. The Beasties were inducted into the Rock & Roll Hall of Fame.

   B. Yauch's stage name was "Buddhist" because he actually was a Buddhist.

   C. The group switched record labels from Def Jam to Capitol.

   D. Audiences appreciated the group's behavior and the music.

   E. The Beastie Boys' first recorded song was "Polly Wog Stew."

5. Which would be the best alternative title for this passage?

   A. How Wild Behavior Sells Albums

   B. The Charitable Work of Adam Yauch

   C. Beastie Boys: The Sound of New York City

   D. The Longevity of the Beastie Boys' Music

   E. The Evolution of the Beastie Boys

EXERCISE 4 / MAKING INFERENCES

Choose the best answer.

1. Which of the following is an **auditory** signal associated with driving a car?

   A. the gas gauge

   B. outside odors

   C. a horn blowing

   D. traffic lights

2. Which is the best example of something that fits the definition of **distorted**?

   A. a speech in another language that is translated incorrectly

   B. a tennis match that lasts longer than expected

   C. a news broadcast recorded live in another country

   D. a letter containing an accurate description of an event

3. If someone wrote a book expressing **radical** viewpoints about democracy, people would be LEAST likely to

   A. write essays criticizing it.

   B. think it's boring and unoriginal.

   C. debate about it on the Internet.

   D. prevent it from being taught in schools.

4. Which of the following is an example of something that has **abated**?

   A. a sad memory that cannot be forgotten

   B. a baseball game that lasts eleven innings

   C. loud music that has been turned down

   D. a storm that drenches a farmer's field

5. What is the most likely reason Madonna's fans found the Beastie Boys' performance **repulsive**?

   A. The Beastie Boys had strong political viewpoints.

   B. They thought the Beastie Boys' behavior was inappropriate.

   C. Madonna had turned her fans against the Beastie Boys.

   D. Hip-hop had not yet emerged as a music genre.

EXERCISE 5 / ROOTS, PREFIXES, AND SUFFIXES

Answer the questions below that are designed to help you arrive at some conclusions about word families and origins.

Roots: *nomen*, "name"
     torq/tort, "to twist"

Prefix: *ex–*, "out"

1. Based on your knowledge of the roots in this section, which of the following would be considered a proper use of the word *nomenclature*?

   A. an updated phone operating system

   B. a winding road

   C. a list of plants

   D. a feeling of love for a family member

2. Define the italicized word below using your knowledge of the *ex–* prefix, the *tort* root, and the context of the sentence.

   Sam and Lila used the information they found to *extort* a lot of money from Terrell.

   _____

3. Read the description and then answer the question that follows.

   The first group of acrobats climbed ropes at lightning speed. The people in the second group bent themselves into shapes like pretzels. Finally, a trio in yellow sequined suits balanced on a tower of stacked chairs.

   Which group is made up of *contortionists*?

   _____

4. In your wallet, you might have various *denominations* of bills. Which of the following is an example of that?

   A. You have nothing but $1 bills.

   B. They total more than $20.

   C. You have a $5, a $10, and a $20.

   D. Some are old, and some are new.

FREESTYLE

IT'S 1997 IN Los Angeles. Marshall Mathers steps out in front of a wild, screaming audience. There's absolute **bedlam** at the Rap Olympics. Mathers grabs the mic while the DJ starts the beat. The other **hapless** emcee stands aside, looking pitiably defenseless as he is sized up. Mathers immediately goes on the attack, accusing the other emcee of writing lyrics ahead of time.

"What you need to do is practice on your freestyles," Mathers spits, " 'Fore you come out missin' like Snoop Dogg's police files!"

Mathers, as you probably know, will later become Eminem. While Eminem will go on to release many albums—some even reaching Diamond status with sales of 10,000,000 units— he will always be known as one of the greatest freestyle rappers of all time.

So what is freestyling?

Freestyling is unlike any other kind of rap because it is entirely improvised. It usually involves a competition between two dueling emcees, who **parry** insults and verbally **antagonize** each other in front of a crowd. The taunts are vicious, often crude, sometimes including racial slurs to belittle the opponent. Similar to other lyrics in rap, there are often references to what are generally **taboo** topics, including violence, guns, drugs, and other elements related to the dangerous life on the street. While someone might be offended by their vulgarity, the lyrics can also be quite creative. They contain many of the same literary devices used in poetry, such as metaphor and allusion, as well as meter and rhyme. The raps are intended to appeal to the audience, which ultimately decides who the best freestyler is.

Despite what it may appear, the confrontation between the emcees is all a **facade** and not meant to be taken too seriously. However much they seem angered by what is said, there is a mutual understanding among the artists that any **disrespect** is not meant to be taken personally. Emcees who lose control and turn a freestyle battle into real violence are heavily criticized. It is actually quite common for emcees to leave on friendly terms and even congratulate each other after a good performance.

While there are sometimes formal events like the Rap Olympics, freestyle battles are usually casual, and they take place in different places in the neighborhood like parks and community centers. The music may be mixed on sophisticated equipment like turntables, but it can also be played on other **random** sound systems like car stereos. Some places become well known and attract aspiring artists who get together to practice and socialize on a regular basis.

Many of the rappers become locally popular and **envisage** themselves becoming famous nationally, or even worldwide. The people who have been freestyling for many years serve as mentors to the newer generation of rappers; however, the older rappers are sometimes looked down upon. The goal of most freestylers is to eventually make it in the music industry. Those who don't end up rapping professionally are seen by other freestylers as people who have been **deluding** themselves and don't have enough talent to get a record deal.

Just in case you didn't know, Marshall Mathers lost that '97 Rap Olympics to Otherwize.

Yeah…I don't know who that is, either.

EXERCISE 1 / WORD LIST

Use the context in which the word is used to determine what the word probably means. Write a brief definition in the space provided.

1. **antagonize:** _____

   It usually involves a competition between two dueling emcees, who parry insults and verbally **antagonize** each other in front of a crowd.

2. **bedlam:** _____

   Marshall Mathers steps out in front of a wild, screaming audience. There's absolute **bedlam** at the Rap Olympics.

3. **delude:** _____

   The goal of most freestylers is to eventually make it in the music industry. Those who don't end up rapping professionally are seen by other freestylers as people who have been **deluding** themselves and don't have enough talent to get a record deal.

4. **disrespect:** _____

   However much they seem angered by what is said, there is a mutual understanding among the artists that any **disrespect** is not meant to be taken personally.

5. **envisage:** _____

   Many of the rappers become locally popular and **envisage** themselves becoming famous nationally, or even worldwide.

6. **facade:** _____

   Despite what it may appear, the confrontation between the emcees is all a **facade** and not meant to be taken too seriously.

7. **hapless:** _____

   The other **hapless** emcee stands aside, looking pitiably defenseless as he is sized up. Mathers immediately goes on the attack, accusing the other emcee of writing lyrics ahead of time.

8. **parry:** _____

It usually involves a competition between two dueling emcees, who **parry** insults back and forth and verbally antagonize each other in front of a crowd.

9. **random:** _____

The music may be mixed on sophisticated equipment like turntables, but it can also be played on other **random** sound systems like car stereos.

10. **taboo:** _____

Similar to other lyrics in rap, there are often references to what are generally **taboo** topics, including violence, guns, drugs, and other elements related to the dangerous life on the street.

EXERCISE 2 / USING WORDS IN CONTEXT

Fill in the blank with the vocabulary word that best completes the sentence. In some cases, you may need to change the tense or form of a verb or the number of a noun.

parry	hapless	facade	envisage	antagonize
taboo	bedlam	random	delude	disrespect

1. When Nas didn't show up to record a verse for Jay-Z's album *Reasonable Doubt*, Jay-Z believed it to be an act of great _____.

2. Darlene is such a skilled martial artist that I'm sure she will _____ all of Pablo's punches with ease.

3. We lost each other in the _____ of the subway station, where three hundred frantic people ran to and from the trains.

4. I think it's amusing how Kanye West likes to _____ himself into thinking he will someday become the president.

5. Beneath the _____ of a grouchy old woman, Maggie is a kind-hearted kindergarten teacher who loves children.

6. I never would have _____ myself being brave enough to go whitewater rafting on the Colorado River.

7. Lil' Kim violated so many fashion _____ at the MTV Music Awards that some fans considered boycotting her music.

8. The _____ student forgot her umbrella and got soaked in the rain on her way to class.

9. The _____ string of sounds in Missy Elliott's "Work It" is actually the previous line played in reverse.

10. If you really want to _____ your sister and get into an argument, tell her that her orange prom dress is ugly.

EXERCISE 3 / READING COMPREHENSION AND ANALYSIS

Select the best answers to the following questions based on a close and thorough reading of "Freestyle."

1. The purpose of the first three paragraphs in this passage is to

   A. illustrate the complexity of Eminem's lyrics in a freestyle rap battle.

   B. suggest that there was true hatred between Eminem and the other emcee.

   C. introduce the concept of freestyle that will eventually lead to an explanation of it.

   D. show why Eminem ended up losing the Rap Olympics to Otherwize.

   E. provide a brief biography on Eminem and his road to success in the music industry.

2. The use of the word *spits* in Paragraph 2 is an example of

   A. metaphor.

   B. onomatopoeia.

   C. allusion.

   D. understatement.

   E. alliteration.

3. Which of the following contradicts one of the statements in Paragraph 6?

   A. The media creates and reports false rivalry between the artists.

   B. Becoming physically violent is not acceptable in rap battles.

   C. The insults used are just a part of the contest, not genuine criticisms.

   D. Freestyle artists give each other advice on how to improve.

   E. Most of the rap battles result in long-lasting feuds between emcees.

4. Read the following sentence:

"Because of this, the contestants make references and statements that they think will be entertaining to the people present."

This sentence would be best placed at the end of which paragraph?

A. Paragraph 1

B. Paragraph 4

C. Paragraph 5

D. Paragraph 6

E. Paragraph 7

5. The last two sentences of the passage serve to

A. bring the passage full-circle.

B. reintroduce the central theme of freestyle.

C. encourage the reader to do additional research.

D. make a pun on the word *otherwise*.

E. diminish Mathers's freestyling abilities.

EXERCISE 4 / MAKING INFERENCES

Choose the best answer.

1. You would most likely encounter **bedlam**

A. in a full lecture hall during a science class.

B. while waiting in line to buy tickets to a movie.

C. on a tour going through a national historical site.

D. in a store that is selling smartphones for half-price.

2. Which of the following is the best example of the word **parry**?

A. The governor parried questions about raising taxes around election time.

B. The baseball player parried the ball and ran to first base.

C. The writers parried a few ideas about what articles should be in the magazine.

D. The two women parried compliments about each other's fashion.

3. With which statement would the author most likely agree?

   A. Rap and poetry share many of the same elements.

   B. Because Eminem lost, he didn't deserve the fame he received.

   C. Freestyling is a superior type of rap because it is made up on the spot.

   D. People who cannot make it professionally in rap need to quit freestyling.

4. What is the best example of something **taboo** in a foreign country?

   A. forgetting your luggage at the airport

   B. not speaking the language of the country

   C. getting lost in the middle of the city

   D. ignoring the customs of the country

5. Which statement is the best example of Karl **deluding** himself?

   A. If I continue to work at it, I should get into art school.

   B. I'll make the football team with only a little practice.

   C. I can take care of your house while you're away on vacation.

   D. I doubt that my answers on the math final were correct.

EXERCISE 5 / ROOTS, PREFIXES, AND SUFFIXES

Answer the questions below that are designed to help you arrive at some conclusions about word families and origins.

1. *Agon* is the Greek word meaning "contest, struggle." Playwrights in ancient Greece entered contests to have their plays judged the best, just as athletes competed to see who was the fastest and strongest. From these contests, we get words that we now use when talking about literature: *protagonist* and *antagonist*.

   The prefix *protos–* means "first."
   The prefix *anti–* means "against."

   Use the sentence below and your knowledge of *protos–*, *anti–*, and *agon* to answer the questions.

   > The movie's *protagonist* has to make a decision that almost costs him his life. Meanwhile, his *antagonist* is getting ready to betray him.

   A. Which word probably means "main character"?

   _____

   B. What do you think the word *antagonist* means?

   _____

2. **Envisage** comes from the Latin word *videre*, *visum*, meaning "to see." From *videre*, *visum* we get the roots *vid* and *vis*.

   What word means "not able to be seen"? _____

3. Fill in the blank with a word that uses the root *agon*.

   After the rattlesnake bit Stephanie, she suffered _____ for hours.

4. The prefix *re–* means "again."
   The prefix *super–* means "over."

   Using the prefixes above and your knowledge of the *vis* root, explain how we get the definition of each of the following words:

   revise: "to edit" = _____
   supervise: "to manage" = _____

DR. DRE

ANDRE ROMELLE YOUNG was born on February 18, 1965; both his parents had backgrounds in music, which may explain his **penchant** for it. He grew up in Compton, California, a city **notorious** for its gang activity. Andre frequently changed schools in an effort to avoid violence and wisely chose music over gangs. He turned his family's home into a studio, using a music mixer to sample songs and create new sounds. Fulfilling his desire for mixing music, he began performing as a DJ at clubs in Los Angeles, calling himself Dr. J after his favorite basketball player. While working as a DJ, he formed the group World Class Wreckin' Cru; their music was a blend of electronic pop and hip-hop. Young then changed his stage name to Dr. Dre, the Master of Mixology.

In 1986, Dre teamed up with rapper O'Shea "Ice Cube" Jackson, and they wrote verses for Eric "Eazy-E" Wright, the founder of Ruthless Records. Together, these artists formed the **nucleus** of N.W.A; MC Ren and DJ Yella also joined the group. With their 1988 album, *Straight Outta Compton*, N.W.A brought the new hip-hop style called "gangsta rap" into the mainstream. Dr. Dre may have avoided joining a gang in his youth, but he, and other similar rappers, still celebrated gang violence and drug use. Rappers, including Ice Cube, bragged about the **carnage** they supposedly caused by shooting rival musicians. Not surprisingly, N.W.A was a highly controversial group; parents, politicians, and even some rap fans **denounced** their lyrics. Yet, despite its objectionable content and lack of radio play, *Straight Outta Compton* sold 750,000 copies, even returning to the charts in 2015. The gangsta rap that Dr. Dre helped create remained popular for years.

The violence in N.W.A's music seemed to bleed into Young's personal life; in 1991 and 1992, he faced multiple assault charges. After dealing with the accusations through fines and community service, Dre left N.W.A and cofounded Death Row Records with Suge Knight. This label started strong, with Dr. Dre's highly rated album, *The Chronic*, which featured a new style—gangsta rap lyrics played over music sampled from 1970s funk songs. Although it is **debatable** whether Young invented this subgenre, because other hip-hop artists had recorded similar music earlier, he certainly popularized the sound. In *The Chronic*, Dre also introduced the world to Snoop Dogg, then an unknown **neophyte**, who rapped with Dre on multiple tracks. After *The Chronic*, Young focused primarily on producing other artists, yet the beats he laid out continued to influence the sound of hip-hop.

For the next few years, Dr. Dre produced soundtracks and worked with rappers, including Ice Cube and Tupac. Despite the record company's success, a **rift** grew between Dre and Suge Knight; by 1996, Young found Knight's violent manner of conducting business **contemptible**. Dre left their label and formed Aftermath Entertainment. He soon produced a compilation album, *Dr. Dre Presents… The Aftermath*. While the single "Been There Done That" became a hit, the record as a whole received only fair reviews. Aftermath Entertainment did not prosper until Dre signed Eminem in 1999. Since then, he has worked with many hip-hop artists who became well-known **celebrities**, including 50 Cent, Busta Rhymes, and Kendrick Lamar.

Dre continued his business success by cofounding Beats Electronics and debuting his headphone line, Beats by Dre, in 2008. When he sold Beats to Apple, Inc. in 2014, Dr. Dre became the world's richest hip-hop artist, with a net worth of approximately $800 million. Although Dre retired from rapping after his 2015 album, *Compton*, his career illustrates how hip-hop artists can become successful businesspeople, especially if they are talented and able to recognize others' skill and potential mass appeal.

EXERCISE 1 / WORD LIST

Use the context in which the word is used to determine what the word probably means. Write a brief definition in the space provided.

1. **carnage:** _____

   Rappers, including Ice Cube, bragged about the **carnage** they supposedly caused by shooting rival musicians.

2. **celebrity:** _____

   Since then, he has worked with many hip-hop artists who became well-known **celebrities**, including 50 Cent, Busta Rhymes, and Kendrick Lamar.

3. **contemptible:** _____

   …Young found Knight's violent manner of conducting business **contemptible**.

4. **debatable:** _____

   Although it is **debatable** whether Young invented this subgenre, because other hip-hop artists had recorded similar music earlier, he certainly popularized the sound.

5. **denounce:** _____

   N.W.A was a highly controversial group; parents, politicians, and even some rap fans **denounced** their lyrics.

6. **neophyte:** _____

   In *The Chronic*, Dre also introduced the world to Snoop Dogg, then an unknown **neophyte**, who rapped with Dre on multiple tracks.

7. **notorious:** _____

   He grew up in Compton, California, a city **notorious** for its gang activity. Andre frequently changed schools in an effort to avoid violence…

8. **nucleus:** _____

   Together, these artists formed the **nucleus** of N.W.A; MC Ren and DJ Yella also joined the group.

9. **penchant:** _____

Andre Romelle Young was born on February 18, 1965; both his parents had backgrounds in music, which may explain his **penchant** for it.

10. **rift:** _____

Despite the record company's success, a **rift** grew between Dre and Suge Knight; by 1996, Young found Knight's violent manner of conducting business contemptible.

EXERCISE 2 / USING WORDS IN CONTEXT

Fill in the blank with the vocabulary word that best completes the sentence. In some cases, you may need to change the tense or form of a verb or the number of a noun.

rift	penchant	notorious	neophyte	debatable
celebrity	denounce	nucleus	carnage	contemptible

1. Will Smith had a _____ for humorous, non-threatening songs, which made him stand out against the gangsta rap image that other artists had.

2. Police in a helicopter flew over the destruction and _____ the tornado had caused to the small town.

3. When I was sitting at the table in that restaurant, a _____ asked if he could take an empty chair to use at his own table: It was Grandmaster Flash.

4. The _____ between two members of N.W.A grew too wide for them to heal, and the group broke up; some people said it happened because of too much success.

5. Pablo was a complete _____ and knew nothing about antiques, so he overpaid for the old chair at the auction.

6. The principal announced, "Bullying is _____, and this school will expel anyone who participates in it!"

7. It may be _____ whether Prince Rogers Nelson or Sean John Combs had more nicknames, but Prince's unpronounceable symbol is certainly weirder than "P. Diddy."

8. Even though most fans enjoy the lead guitarist in a band, musicians believe that the drummer and bassist form the _____ of the group.

9. Although Kendrick says his dog is harmless, it is _____ for growling at and frightening children.

10. During the school's "Battle of the Bands," The X Chords were disqualified for _____ their main competition, Sonic Tonsils.

EXERCISE 3 / READING COMPREHENSION AND ANALYSIS

Select the best answers to the following questions based on a close and thorough reading of "Dr. Dre."

1. Which of the following statements about Dr. Dre is FALSE?

   A. His first stage name came from a basketball player's name.

   B. He worked on albums by 50 Cent and Kendrick Lamar.

   C. *The Chronic* blended 1970s funk samples with newer gangsta rap.

   D. Snoop Dogg helped him become a famous rap star.

   E. When Apple bought Beats by Dre, his worth increased by about $800 million.

2. Which is the best summary of the main idea of the passage?

   A. Dre achieved a great deal of success by selling his headphone company to Apple.

   B. Dre worked with many different people, and he helped them become successful.

   C. Dre's time with N.W.A made him a superstar in the world of gangsta rap.

   D. Even without the help of Dr. Dre, many rap artists would have achieved success.

   E. Dre began to see that his future was primarily in producing rap, not performing.

3. What would be the best substitution for the word *yet* in this sentence: "After *The Chronic*, Young focused primarily on producing other artists, yet the beats he laid out continued to influence the sound of hip-hop"?

   A. because

   B. up to then

   C. besides

   D. in addition

   E. but

4. Which sentence in Paragraph 3 best supports this fact in the final sentence of that paragraph: "The gangsta rap that Dr. Dre helped create remained popular for years"?

   A. "Yet, despite its objectionable content and lack of radio play, *Straight Outta Compton* sold 750,000 copies, even returning to the charts in 2015."

   B. "Not surprisingly, N.W.A was a highly controversial group; parents, politicians, and even some rap fans denounced their lyrics."

   C. "In 1986, Dre teamed up with rapper O'Shea 'Ice Cube' Jackson, and they wrote verses for Eric 'Eazy-E' Wright, the founder of Ruthless Records."

   D. "Rappers, including Ice Cube, bragged about the carnage they supposedly caused by shooting rival musicians."

   E. "With their 1988 album, *Straight Outta Compton*, N.W.A brought the new hip-hop style called 'gangsta rap' into the mainstream."

5. What does the author specifically NOT tell you about Dr. Dre in this passage?

   A. Dr. Dre worked with many people who became famous rap musicians.

   B. Dr. Dre quit World Class Wreckin' Cru to produce *Straight Outta Compton*.

   C. *Dr. Dre Presents…The Aftermath* came about after problems with Suge Knight.

   D. Snoop Dogg and Dr. Dre rapped together on a few tracks for *The Chronic* album.

   E. The last album that Dr. Dre rapped on was named after *Straight Outta Compton*.

EXERCISE 4 / MAKING INFERENCES

Choose the best answer.

1. In which example would the person best be classified as a **neophyte**?

    A. An astronomer discovers water on Mars the first time he looks at the planet.

    B. A young girl is able to fly her kite the first time she tries to do it.

    C. A girl watches a TV show for the first time and decides it's not as good as other shows.

    D. A musician can play a piece of music on the piano the first time he tries.

2. What inference are you logically able to make about Ice Cube, based on information in the passage?

    A. He was not an original member of N.W.A.

    B. He bragged about shooting rival gang members.

    C. He faced charges of assault more than once.

    D. He and Dr. Dre worked together only one time.

3. Which example would show a **penchant** for something?

    A. You and your best friend have an argument over a concert.

    B. Your teacher gave out homework nine weekends in a row.

    C. You tried skiing but gave up after falling ten times.

    D. You haven't liked dressing up for Halloween in years.

4. What is the best example of the word **contemptible**?

    A. throwing a plastic cup on the ground

    B. arguing with parents over doing chores

    C. driving fifteen miles over the speed limit

    D. stealing from a charitable organization

5. A *rift* is most likely to occur after a

    A. lightning storm.

    B. plane flight.

    C. bad argument.

    D. birthday party.

EXERCISE 5 / ROOTS, PREFIXES, AND SUFFIXES

Answer the questions below that are designed to help you arrive at some conclusions about word families and origins.

1. The root *carn* means "flesh," and the root *vor* means "to eat." Use this information to fill in the blank in the following sentence:

   Anything that that eats flesh or meat, therefore, can be classified as a _____.

2. The prefix *re–* means "again," and the prefix *in–* means "into." Use this information to fill in the blank in the following sentence:

   If someone is literally "born into flesh again," he or she has been _____.

3. The root *nunc, nounc* means "to speak," "to tell," or "to announce." Fill in the following blanks with the right forms.

Verb	Noun
1. pronounce	_____
2. _____	denunciation
3. _____	annunciation
4. enunciate	_____

EAST COAST/WEST COAST

MANY HIP-HOP enthusiasts are familiar with the rivalry between the East Coast and West Coast rap industries and support one side over the other. Do more fans prefer a focus on complex lyrics, typical of East Coast rap? Or do they find the West Coast technique more appealing, with its stronger emphasis on music and rhythm? Can they even **perceive** a difference? It's possible, however, that their preference is connected to a different element, such as the rift between the record labels and artists on the opposite coasts. The conflict is complicated. It began with the competition for album sales and media attention in the 1980s. It then increased in **magnitude** because of the bitter feud between Christopher Wallace ("Biggie Smalls" or "The Notorious B.I.G.) and Tupac Shakur.

When rap started becoming more popular and expanded beyond New York City, newer artists emerged in places like Compton and Los Angeles. Recording studios and rappers in the East became resentful that their publicity was lessening and their income dwindling. Despite the developing hostility in the industry, Biggie, from the East Coast, and Tupac, from the West Coast, became close friends. Tupac, already a hip-hop star, acted as a mentor to Biggie. At that point in time, Biggie was a young man with **phenomenal** talent, but was still somewhat unknown. Unfortunately, a vicious feud developed between them.

While in the lobby of Quad Recording Studios on November 30, 1994, Tupac was shot five times and robbed. Although there was no proof, Tupac believed that the founder of Bad Boy Records, Sean Combs (also known as "Puff Daddy" and many other aliases) and Biggie were responsible. Later, Biggie released a song titled "Who Shot Ya?" Tupac believed that the lyrics were about him personally. In return, he wrote "Hit 'Em Up," a **blatant** and undeniable attack on Biggie and Combs.

In 1995, Tupac's gangsta image was reinforced when he was **prosecuted** for sexual assault and incarcerated. While in prison, he befriended Marion "Suge" Knight, who paid Tupac's bail and signed him to a deal with Death Row Records. Suge became involved in the hip-hop rivalry and blamed Combs for the death of an associate, Jake Robles. This accusation helped intensify the hostility between Tupac and Biggie.

The battle reached its **pinnacle** in 1996 and 1997, when two events occurred that changed the hip-hop world forever. On September 6, 1996, Tupac and Suge attended a Mike Tyson boxing match in Las Vegas. When they left and were stopped at a light, an unknown person in another car opened fire, and Tupac was hit by four bullets. He was rushed to the hospital for treatment, but died of internal bleeding six days later. Biggie attempted to **mitigate** the conflict and stop additional violence, but nobody knows whether his actions came from a genuine desire for peace or a fear for his own safety. Unfortunately, before any progress could be made, he died on March 9, 1997, under shockingly similar circumstances. As he was driving away from a *Vibe Magazine* after-party with his crew, shots shattered the window. One of the bullets proved to be **lethal**, and Biggie Smalls died almost immediately.

Fans were **dejected** as they again mourned the loss of a superstar. Police believe that the murders are connected, but there is no proof. Controversies about their deaths continue, even many years later. In addition, the media has also been largely criticized for **exploiting** the rivalry to attract readers and viewers. The East Coast/West Coast battle is no longer as severe as it had been, but memories of the bloodshed and unnecessary deaths still haunt the hip-hop community and its fans.

EXERCISE 1 / WORD LIST

Use the context in which the word is used to determine what the word probably means. Write a brief definition in the space provided.

1. **blatant:** _____

   In return, he wrote "Hit 'Em Up," a **blatant** and undeniable attack on Biggie and Combs.

2. **dejected:** _____

   Fans were **dejected** as they again mourned the loss of a superstar.

3. **exploit:** _____

   In addition, the media has also been largely criticized for **exploiting** the rivalry to attract readers and viewers.

4. **lethal:** _____

   One of the bullets proved to be **lethal**, and Biggie Smalls died almost immediately.

5. **magnitude:** _____

   It then increased in **magnitude** because of the bitter feud between Christopher Wallace ("Biggie Smalls" or "The Notorious B.I.G.) and Tupac Shakur.

6. **mitigate:** _____

   Biggie attempted to **mitigate** the conflict and stop additional violence, but nobody knows whether his actions came from a genuine desire for peace or a fear for his own safety.

7. **perceive:** _____

   Do more fans prefer a focus on complex lyrics, typical of East Coast rap? Or do they find the West Coast technique more appealing, with its stronger emphasis on music and rhythm? Can they even **perceive** a difference?

8. **phenomenal:** _____

   At that point in time, Biggie was a young man with **phenomenal** talent, but was still somewhat unknown.

9. **pinnacle:** _____

The battle reached its **pinnacle** in 1996 and 1997, when two events occurred that changed the hip-hop world forever.

10. **prosecute:** _____

In 1995, Tupac's gangsta image was reinforced when he was **prosecuted** for sexual assault and incarcerated.

EXERCISE 2 / USING WORDS IN CONTEXT

Fill in the blank with the vocabulary word that best completes the sentence. In some cases, you may need to change the tense or form of a verb or the number of a noun.

lethal	blatant	exploit	mitigate	phenomenal
perceive	dejected	prosecute	pinnacle	magnitude

1. Steph wasn't worried that the police would _____ her for breaking into her neighbor's house to rescue their dog.

2. While some of his friends might not _____ J. Cole as intelligent, he graduated from St. John's University with a 3.8 GPA.

3. The restaurant's sushi has such a(n) _____ taste that it was voted the best Japanese food in Philadelphia.

4. Despite having lost, DJ Khaled didn't seem too _____ when Chance the Rapper won the Grammy for Best Rap Album.

5. The vendor knew how to _____ the thirst of the visitors on the hot day by doubling the price of the water he was selling.

6. The album *Confessions* was the _____ of Usher's career; it sold over 20 million copies worldwide.

7. People didn't anticipate the _____ of Big Boi's success when he started a solo project that was immensely popular with fans.

8. The public knew the governor was telling _____ lies because he couldn't back up his claims with facts or statistics.

9. The dentist gave me some medication to _____ the pain from having my wisdom teeth removed.

10. The liquid that Juliet drank wasn't _____, but it put her into a deep sleep for nearly two days, and she did seem to be dead.

EXERCISE 3 / READING COMPREHENSION AND ANALYSIS

Select the best answers to the following questions based on a close and thorough reading of "East Coast/West Coast."

1. The intent of this passage is to

   A. amuse.

   B. inform.

   C. persuade.

   D. insult.

   E. instruct.

2. The information in this passage is organized by

   A. theme.

   B. importance.

   C. chronology.

   D. persuasion.

   E. contradiction.

3. What is the reason the East Coast artists saw their "income dwindling"?

   A. East Coast artists were not being signed by record labels.

   B. East Coast artists had lost two of their most popular stars.

   C. West Coast artists received more publicity than the East Coast artists did.

   D. West Coast artists did not write as complex lyrics as the East Coast artists did.

   E. West Coast artists' sales were increasing at the expense of East Coast sales.

4. What was the initial cause of the feud between Biggie and Tupac?

    A. the influence of Suge Knight

    B. the East Coast/West Coast rivalry

    C. the attack on Tupac

    D. the murder of Jake Robles

    E. the rap "Hit 'Em Up"

5. The phrase "shots shattered the window" is an example of which of the following literary devices?

    A. alliteration

    B. metaphor

    C. hyperbole

    D. personification

    E. simile

EXERCISE 4 / MAKING INFERENCES

Choose the best answer.

1. What does the "difference" in Paragraph 1 refer to?

    A. artists on the East Coast and West Coast

    B. musical styles unique to each region

    C. the landscape of the coasts

    D. the music of Tupac and Biggie Smalls

2. What would be a **blatant** way someone could cheat at a card game?

    A. determine the odds of getting a card

    B. deal himself two extra cards

    C. peek at another player's hand

    D. hide an ace up his sleeve

3. If you wanted to **mitigate** your fear of public speaking, you might

    A. never participate in class discussions.

    B. post more on social media.

    C. practice in front of a mirror.

    D. call your friends rather than text them.

4. A person might feel **dejected** if he

    A. loses his phone on a roller coaster.

    B. has a very happy marriage.

    C. spends a lot of time at the gym.

    D. wakes up early in the morning.

5. You might **exploit** a person's generosity by

    A. repaying the debts that you have owed her for a long time.

    B. offering to drive her wherever she desired to go.

    C. buying her expensive birthday presents year after year.

    D. suggesting she pay the bill at lunch three times in a row.

EXERCISE 5 / ROOTS, PREFIXES, AND SUFFIXES

Answer the questions below that are designed to help you arrive at some conclusions about word families and origins.

1. The root *ject* means "to throw." Add a prefix to this root in order to come up with a word that fits the definition:

   _____ *ject* = to refuse to accept or agree to

   _____ *ject* = an undertaking; something that requires effort

   _____ *ject* = to put a vaccine into the body

   _____ *ject* = to throw out with force

   Now, match each of these words to a situation in which you might use it.

   The community began building a new skyscraper. _____

   The pilot escaped the plane before it crashed. _____

   He needed some medicine, but couldn't swallow it. _____

   That apple is soft, so let's not buy it. _____

2. Based on your knowledge of the *ject* root, which item is most likely to be a *projectile*?

   A. book

   B. frisbee

   C. car

   D. bird

3. The root *magn* means "large."

   Carla became a business *magnate* when she moved to Toledo.

   From your knowledge of the *magn* root, Carla

   A. was an expert in marketing.

   B. began teaching a business course.

   C. got a job with a major corporation.

   D. became president of a bank.

4. The root *anim* means "heart, spirit, soul." If we say Mr. Reese is *magnanimous*, we most likely mean he is

   A. generous.

   B. outgoing.

   C. funny.

   D. mean.

TUPAC

MANY THINGS COME to mind upon hearing the name Tupac Shakur. To the law, he was a **nefarious** criminal; to his fans, he was the voice of the inner city. He had an extensive criminal record, consisting of everything from drug possession to sexual assault. Tattooed across his chest were the words "Thug Life," which may have seemed an accurate description of his lifestyle. However, hidden beneath the **illusion** of just a "gangsta" was a man few people would recognize—a well-read intellectual and passionate artist.

Tupac was born in Harlem, New York, as Lesane Parish Crooks. His mother, an activist, renamed him Tupac after Túpac Amaru II, a famous Peruvian revolutionary. He took the name Shakur from the father of his half-sister. Tupac developed a strong interest in the performing arts early on, acting in a theatrical version of *A Raisin in the Sun* at the age of thirteen. A few years later, his family moved to Baltimore, where he enrolled in the Baltimore School for the Arts. He began a formal education in both music and dance, but because of the crime in the area, his family moved to Marin City, California.

Tupac's entrance into the hip-hop world may seem **fatalistic** and destined to happen, but it was more likely his charisma and intelligence. While in a park in Marin City, he noticed a woman, Leila Steinberg, reading an autobiography by Winnie Mandela. Tupac had studied the book, and he and Steinberg spent hours discussing it. Little did he know that Steinberg was a singer and dancer and ran workshops on the Arts. Her positive first impression of Tupac **impelled** her to help him get a job in the music industry, and she introduced him to Digital Underground, a rap crew; his job simply involved moving equipment on and off the stage. Later, he worked as a D.U. emcee and back-up dancer, usually demonstrating great **humility**,

as opposed to the attitude he would express in his future works.

Mandela's book was just one of many that Tupac had read; surprisingly, he was also a big fan of Edgar Allan Poe, Victor Hugo, and Shakespeare. What he read had an influence on him, helping him **hone** his style and develop his **diction** and mastery of words. Many of the ideas he impulsively jotted down throughout the day were later developed into raps. He released four albums during his lifetime, all of which became widely popular. The most famous, *All Eyez on Me* (1996), has sold over 10 million copies.

Using his celebrity status to help others, Tupac became a **benefactor** of local communities, including helping to set up a youth center for at-risk teens in South Central LA and regularly reaching out to his fans. In one instance, the parents of a boy contacted a radio station and asked if there was a way to get in touch with Tupac. Their 11-year-old had terminal muscular dystrophy, and his last wish was to meet his idol. Tupac immediately went to the hospital and talked to the boy for a few hours, showing great sympathy and emotion. After the boy passed away, Tupac renamed his record label Joshua's Dream.

In 1996, Tupac's life was tragically cut short. Sad and grieving fans **lamented** his death, and many honored his memory through art and music. Tupac had been such a productive writer during his lifetime that many of his previously unreleased songs were collected and made into albums; in addition, a selection of his poetry was published as a book, *The Rose That Grew from Concrete*. While it is true that Tupac was a **fallible** man, filled with faults, it would be unfair to ignore his good deeds that changed people's lives.

EXERCISE 1 / WORD LIST

Use the context in which the word is used to determine what the word probably means. Write a brief definition in the space provided.

1. **benefactor:** _____

   Using his celebrity status to help others, Tupac became a **benefactor** of local communities, including helping to set up a youth center for at-risk teens in South Central LA and regularly reaching out to his fans.

2. **diction:** _____

   What he read had an influence on him, helping him hone his style and develop his **diction** and mastery of words.

3. **fallible:** _____

   While it is true that Tupac was a **fallible** man, filled with faults, it would be unfair to ignore his good deeds that changed people's lives.

4. **fatalistic:** _____

   Tupac's entrance into the hip-hop world may seem **fatalistic** and destined to happen, but it was more likely his charisma and intelligence.

5. **hone:** _____

   What he read had an influence on him, helping him **hone** his style and develop his diction and mastery of words.

6. **humility:** _____

   Later, he worked as a D.U. emcee and back-up dancer, usually demonstrating great **humility**, as opposed to the attitude he would express in his future works.

7. **illusion:** _____

   However, hidden beneath the **illusion** of just a "gangsta" was a man few people would recognize—a well-read intellectual and passionate artist.

8. **impel:** _____

   Her positive first impression of Tupac **impelled** her to help him get a job in the music industry, and she introduced him to Digital Underground, a rap crew...

9. **lament:** _____

Sad and grieving fans **lamented** his death, and many honored his memory through art and music.

10. **nefarious:** _____

To the law, he was a **nefarious** criminal; to his fans, he was the voice of the inner city.

EXERCISE 2 / USING WORDS IN CONTEXT

Fill in the blank with the vocabulary word that best completes the sentence. In some cases, you may need to change the tense or form of a verb or the number of a noun.

impel	hone	diction	illusion	nefarious
fatalistic	fallible	humility	lament	benefactor

1. Suge Knight became famous for _____ and violent negotiation tactics when making deals with artists that benefitted him more than it did the musicians.

2. The writer demonstrated _____ when he credited his success to his supportive fans instead of to his talent.

3. Some students say that poetry is difficult because the _____ is hard to understand.

4. In order to _____ his freestyling abilities, Jay-Z used to have rap battles with others in his neighborhood.

5. Lana thought everything in life was _____, and she frequently went to a fortune teller for advice.

6. One characteristic of a tragic hero is that he is _____ and has one fatal flaw that leads to his downfall.

7. The comments Christina Aguilera made about Eminem _____ him to insult her in one of his raps.

8. Dan's rich aunt was his _____ and paid for his new car and college tuition.

9. A hologram of Tupac after he died gave the _____ that he was onstage with Snoop Dogg at a 2012 music festival.

10. Sarah _____ the fact that her best friend was leaving to go to college in another country.

EXERCISE 3 / READING COMPREHENSION AND ANALYSIS

Select the best answers to the following questions based on a close and thorough reading of "Tupac."

1. Which of the following best summarizes the introductory paragraph?

    A. Tupac committed many crimes, which ranged from drug possession to sexual assault.

    B. Tupac's intellect and writing talent excuse him from the crimes he has committed.

    C. Themes in hip-hop are represented not only in music and poetry, but also as tattoos on the human body.

    D. In order to be recognized as a "gangsta," a person must have a certain reputation and lifestyle.

    E. Many people dismiss Tupac as just a criminal, but he was also a smart, talented person.

2. What inspired Leila Steinberg to get Tupac into the music industry?

    A. He understood the importance of Mandela's part in history.

    B. He was well read, and she was impressed by his knowledge.

    C. Steinberg was interested in signing new artists to her record label.

    D. Steinberg liked hearing his raps and reading the poetry he showed her.

    E. Steinberg saw that he had a strong determination to become famous.

3. Which of the following statements about Tupac Shakur is FALSE?

    A. He failed classes at the Baltimore School for the Arts.

    B. He performed in *A Raisin in the Sun* when he was thirteen.

    C. He was a member of a rap group called Digital Underground.

    D. He would try to write down his ideas throughout the day.

    E. He has a poetry book called *The Rose That Grew from Concrete.*

4. What does the information about the 11-year-old boy contribute to the passage?

   A. It provides an example of someone who would be considered an "at-risk teen."

   B. It demonstrates a way in which music can have a positive effect on people.

   C. It supports the fact that Tupac did charitable work and helped people he didn't know personally.

   D. It illustrates the way in which radio stations can be a link between artists and their fans.

   E. It shows how young people make the mistake of idolizing people they shouldn't.

5. The writer wants to add the following sentence to the passage. Choose the best paragraph in which to place it.

   "In fact, he even referenced *Romeo and Juliet* and *Macbeth* in an interview with *LA Times Magazine*."

   A. Paragraph 1

   B. Paragraph 2

   C. Paragraph 3

   D. Paragraph 4

   E. Paragraph 5

EXERCISE 4 / MAKING INFERENCES

Choose the best answer.

1. In what profession would a person be required to use excellent **diction** all the time?

   A. law enforcement

   B. video editing

   C. computer science

   D. online journalism

2. Which of the following plotlines would be considered **fatalistic**?

   A. A deaf woman learns to play the violin.

   B. A young hero fulfills an ancient prophecy.

   C. A man frees an elephant after seeing it abused.

   D. A detective solves a thirty-year-old murder case.

3. In which of the following statements is the speaker demonstrating **humility**?

    A. "Even though I worked very hard, I don't think I deserve this promotion."

    B. "Talking to strangers at parties makes me feel uncomfortable."

    C. "I didn't win first place, but that's only because the judges were biased."

    D. "I understand your point of view, but I still don't agree with you."

4. Which is NOT a correct use of the word **impel**?

    A. The car impelled down the highway.

    B. Josh was impelled to buy a new computer after seeing the ad.

    C. I don't know what impelled her to repaint the room.

    D. Receiving an *F* impelled Olivia to study harder.

5. What inference could correctly be drawn from Tupac's naming his record label "Joshua's Dream"?

    A. The community center where Tupac volunteered was called "Joshua's Dream."

    B. The hospital Tupac visited was called the St. Joshua Children's Hospital.

    C. Joshua is a slang term for a teenager stuck in a bad position.

    D. Joshua was the name of the 11-year-old boy with muscular dystrophy.

EXERCISE 5 / ROOTS, PREFIXES, AND SUFFIXES

Answer the questions below that are designed to help you arrive at some conclusions about word families and origins.

Roots: *pel/puls*, "to drive, to push"
      dict, "to say, to speak"
      hum, "lowly; on the ground"

1. The prefix *bene–* means "good, well." A *malefactor* is the opposite of a **benefactor**, so the prefix *mal–* probably means _____.

2. After the *benediction*, the ceremony was over, and the graduates left the auditorium.

   Based on your knowledge of the *bene–* prefix and its use in the sentence above, a *benediction* is probably

   A. a blessing.

   B. an acceptance speech.

   C. an award.

   D. an announcement.

3. Combine a root or an entire word from this chapter with one of the following prefixes to make a new word that matches the supplied definition.

   The prefix *pre–* means "before."
   The prefix *ex–* means "out."
   The prefix *in–* means "not."
   The prefix *re–* means "back."

   A. to speak about something before it happens: _____

   B. to push back: _____

   C. cannot make a mistake: _____

   D. to push out; to reject: _____

4. **Humility** is the opposite of excessive pride; it literally means a "state of being close to the ground or dirt," or "being low."

   What verb from this same root means "to bring someone down; to embarrass"? _____

HIP-HOP'S FIRSTS

ALTHOUGH HIP-HOP and rap had been around since the 1970s, their entrance into the mainstream media was **belated**, appearing over a decade later. What *was* this new style of music that used turntables instead of instruments? What *did* these lyrics mean with all of their slang terms? *How* exactly did you dance to this new beat? Rap undeniably changed the music industry forever, but it required a few ambitious pioneers to pave the way for this new musical style.

The following are some of rap and hip-hop's "firsts."

First Rap Artist Signed to a Major Record Label:

Kurtis Blow, a former breakdancer and DJ from Harlem, was the first artist to get a record deal with a major record label. Mercury Records signed him in 1979 when he wrote his first single, "Christmas Rappin'," a modern version of the famous "'Twas the Night Before Christmas" poem. Blow, whose given name is Walker, continued his success with his second single, "The Breaks," which went gold, eventually selling more than 500,000 units. The first album to go platinum and sell over 1,000,000 units, however, was Run-D.M.C.'s *King of Rock* in 1985. The success of these albums, however, was just a **prelude**. Many more would later reach multi-platinum and diamond status in the decades to come.

First Rap-Dedicated Radio Station:

Prior to the 1980s, rock dominated the music **queues** on radio stations across the United States. That all changed in 1981 when New York's WRKS-FM, known as 98.7 Kiss-FM, **gratified** the fans' desire for hip-hop by becoming the first station dedicated exclusively to rap and R&B. The station lasted for 31 years until it became **defunct** in 2012. By that point, however, rap and hip-hop had become so popular that there were one or several rap stations in nearly all major US cities.

First Rap Grammy Win(s):

Until 1989, rap music was **snubbed** and unrepresented at the Grammy Awards. There were categories for other genres of music—such as rock, blues, jazz, and even children's music—but not rap! The category for Best Rap Performance was eventually introduced, and DJ Jazzy Jeff and the Fresh Prince won the award for their song "Parent's Just Don't Understand." The category for Best Rap Album wasn't added until 1996. *Poverty's Paradise* by Naughty by Nature was the first winner in that category.

First Hip-Hop/Rap Television Show:

The first television show dedicated to hip-hop and rap was *Yo! MTV Raps* in 1988. Hosted by Fab 5 Freddy, the program was lighthearted, fun, and heavily improvised. It contained many **segments**, including interviews and performances, and it featured rising stars like Salt-N-Pepa, N.W.A, and the Beastie Boys. The show **captivated** audiences and led to increased publicity and record sales for the artists. The creation of *Yo! MTV Raps* was also a momentous occasion in the history of rap because the show made rap music more mainstream.

First Rap/Rock Crossover:

While rap music frequently sampled from other music genres, the first time a rap artist collaborated directly with a rock musician was in 1986 when Run-D.M.C. joined with Aerosmith to do a cover of "Walk This Way." It was a huge success and reached No. 4 on the Pop Charts. Many people even credit it with reviving Aerosmith's career.

All of the successes and "firsts" that have been made over the last few decades have helped integrate rap and hip-hop into popular culture. Only someone who is truly **naïve** would still see it as a **frivolous**, passing fad and not as a true art form. While hip-hop and rap will continue to grow and evolve over the years, special appreciation and thanks should be given to the people who made the groundbreaking first steps into the larger music industry.

EXERCISE 1 / WORD LIST

Use the context in which the word is used to determine what the word probably means. Write a brief definition in the space provided.

1. **belated:** _____

   Although hip-hop and rap had been around since the 1970s, their entrance into the mainstream media was **belated**, appearing over a decade later.

2. **captivate:** _____

   The show **captivated** audiences and led to increased publicity and record sales for the artists.

3. **defunct:** _____

   The station lasted for 31 years until it became **defunct** in 2012. By that point, however, rap and hip-hop had become so popular that there were one or several rap stations in nearly all major US cities.

4. **frivolous:** _____

   Only someone who is truly naïve would still see it as a **frivolous**, passing fad and not as a true art form.

5. **gratify:** _____

   Prior to the 1980s, rock dominated the music queues on radio stations across the United States. That all changed in 1981 when New York's WRKS-FM, known as 98.7 Kiss-FM, **gratified** the fans' desire for hip-hop by becoming the first station dedicated exclusively to rap and R&B.

6. **naïve:** _____

   Only someone who is truly **naïve** would still see it as a frivolous, passing fad and not as a true art form.

7. **prelude:** _____

   The first album to go platinum and sell over 1,000,000 units, however, was Run-D.M.C.'s *King of Rock* in 1985. The success of these albums, however, was just a **prelude**. Many more would later reach multi-platinum and diamond status in the decades to come.

8. **queue:** _____

   Prior to the 1980s, rock dominated the music **queues** on radio stations across the United States. That all changed in 1981 when New York's WRKS-FM, known as 98.7 Kiss-FM, gratified the fans' desire for hip-hop by becoming the first station dedicated exclusively to rap and R&B.

9. **segment:** _____

It contained many **segments**, including interviews and performances, and it featured rising stars like Salt-N-Pepa, N.W.A, and the Beastie Boys.

10. **snub:** _____

Until 1989, rap music was **snubbed** and not represented at the Grammy Awards. There were categories for other genres of music—such as rock, blues, jazz, and even children's music—but not rap!

EXERCISE 2 / USING WORDS IN CONTEXT

Fill in the blank with the vocabulary word that best completes the sentence. In some cases, you may need to change the tense or form of a verb or the number of a noun.

belated	defunct	snub	segment	captivate
gratify	prelude	queue	naïve	frivolous

1. LaFace Records, which released CDs by TLC and OutKast, went _____ and merged with RCA Records in 2011.

2. The heavy rain was just a _____ to the torrential downpour and high winds that the hurricane would bring.

3. The student made such _____ excuses about why she was absent that the teacher couldn't stop laughing.

4. In science class today, we learned that the body of an insect is divided into three _____: the head, the thorax, and the abdomen.

5. Excited fans waited in a _____ almost a half-mile long to get an autograph from Ariana Grande.

6. We were so _____ about computer networks that we had to call a technician to fix the problem.

7. The mother attempted to _____ the screaming child by buying her an ice cream cone.

8. Beyoncé _____ the audience at the 2016 Super Bowl with her amazing singing and dancing skills.

9. Some members of Leaders of the New School felt _____ when Busta Rhymes, the group's lead rapper, was getting all of the publicity.

10. Because the newlyweds had busy work schedules, they took a _____ honeymoon three months after the wedding.

EXERCISE 3 / READING COMPREHENSION AND ANALYSIS

Select the best answers to the following questions based on a close and thorough reading of "Hip-Hop's Firsts."

1. The purpose of the italicized words in Paragraph 1 is to
   A. establish the opinions of the narrator.
   B. express what the reader believes.
   C. present an opposing viewpoint.
   D. emphasize the rhetorical questions.
   E. quote some hip-hop lyrics.

2. This passage has divisions organized by
   A. importance.
   B. topic.
   C. region.
   D. chronology.
   E. cause and effect.

3. What is the author's tone when she says, "There were categories for other genres of music—such as rock, blues, jazz, and even children's music—but not rap!"?
   A. surprised
   B. furious
   C. unconcerned
   D. depressed
   E. hopeful

4. Read the following sentence from this chapter:

   "Only someone who is truly naïve would still see [hip-hop] as a frivolous, passing fad and not as a true art form."

   Which statement from Chapter 5, "Hip-Hop Culture," does NOT support the facts in this sentence?

   A. "Fashion, however, is just a small part of hip-hop culture, which includes not only music, but also other forms of expression like art and dance."

   B. "The spray-painted graffiti in back alleys is not the work of troublemakers with too much time on their hands. Instead, it is a form of art with special meaning."

   C. "Daring graffiti artists can also become famous for painting in dangerous places. They dangle over the sides of buildings and climb over barbed-wire fences."

   D. "Like rap music, it has historical roots. It was inspired by older dances like the cakewalk, lindy-hop, and Charleston, which were in vogue in the late 19th and early 20th centuries."

   E. "Regardless of what your opinion might be on hip-hop culture, it is more than just a passing trend and far more complex than you'd previously assumed."

5. Based on the passage, which of the following statements is FALSE?

   A. Many newer rap artists became famous after appearing on *Yo! MTV Raps*.

   B. Kurtis Blow got his record deal because of "Christmas Rappin'."

   C. There are now many rap-dedicated radio stations in the United States.

   D. *King of Rock*, Run-D.M.C.'s album, went platinum.

   E. The category for Best Rap Performance wasn't added until 1996.

EXERCISE 4 / MAKING INFERENCES

Choose the best answer.

1. Which of the following is an INCORRECT use of the word **belated**?

   A. His belated understanding of climate change came about after he read the report.

   B. In September of this year, Kara held her belated Halloween party.

   C. Mom's belated invitation to the wedding caused us to miss it.

   D. She had to send a belated graduation card because she'd been out of the country.

2. You would most likely find a **queue**

    A. leaving the building after a concert.

    B. waiting to check out at a grocery store.

    C. playing a game of soccer.

    D. sitting in the waiting area of an airport.

3. Gina might **snub** her worst enemy by

    A. spreading rumors behind his back.

    B. confronting him in the hallway.

    C. pretending she doesn't see him.

    D. refusing to give back his books.

4. Which of the following is LEAST likely to be a **prelude** to a movie about deep-sea diving?

    A. a comment about what divers did after the story

    B. a brief explanation of the equipment used

    C. a cartoon about a boy's obsession with fish

    D. a statement about the disappearance of coral reefs

5. Read the following sentence from Paragraph 7:

    "Many people even credit [the recording of "Walk This Way"] with reviving Aerosmith's career."

    Based on what can be inferred from the sentence, which of the following would most likely be true?

    A. Aerosmith benefited more from the single than Run-D.M.C. did.

    B. Run-D.M.C. did not want to record the track with Aerosmith.

    C. The combination of rock and rap was a milestone.

    D. Aerosmith's albums had not been selling well.

EXERCISE 5 / ROOTS, PREFIXES, AND SUFFIXES

Answer the questions below that are designed to help you arrive at some conclusions about word families and origins.

The word **defunct** comes from the prefix *de–*, meaning "down, away," and the root *fung/funct*, which means "to use."

The word **gratify** comes from the Latin word *gratus*, which means "thankful," "pleasing." The root *grat* comes from *gratus*.

1. What word means "the way something is used"? _____

2. A. From your knowledge of the root meaning "thankful" and the sentence below, give the best definition for *ingrate*.

   Eric wanted to exchange his birthday gift for something better, but he feared looking like an *ingrate*.

   _____

   What does the prefix *in–* mean here? _____

   B. From your knowledge of the root meaning "thankful" and the sentence below, give the best definition for *ingratiate*.

   Instead of studying, Michael tried to *ingratiate* himself with the teacher by constantly complimenting her.

   _____

3. The prefix *mal–* means "bad." Add it to the root meaning "to use" to complete the sentence below.

   When the onboard computer _____ioned, oxygen levels in the space capsule dropped.

JAY-Z

LISTEN TO THE radio, turn on the television, or open a magazine and you'll probably come across one of the most famous artists in the music industry today: Jay-Z. You might wonder who or what an "Izzo" is, or maybe what "99 Problems" a multi-millionaire could possibly have. One thing that's clear, however, is that Jay-Z is an artist and businessman conquering the hip-hop world one step at a time.

Shawn "Jay-Z" Carter was born on December 4, 1969, in the dangerous Marcy Projects of Brooklyn, NY. The neighborhood was filled with crime, violence, and drugs, but he took comfort in music. His parents had an enormous collection of albums, and he enjoyed listening to Stevie Wonder, Michael Jackson, and the old Motown classics. He also developed a love of words and read the dictionary with eagerness and **alacrity**. Like other hip-hop artists, he knew it was essential to develop a large vocabulary that could be later **manipulated** to make rhymes. His mother and siblings supported his passion, but weren't particularly fond of being kept awake late at night while he rapped and pounded beats on the dining room table. Even when he was out on the streets, he was at work making music in his head. He didn't always have his notebook with him, so he developed the ability to remember the rhymes until he could write them down later.

While the young man had an amazing talent for rap, he was cautious when entering the music industry. His friends warned him about the **guile** and greed of record companies, many of which **embezzle** money and have no concern for the artists' well-being. Although several company executives tried to **negotiate** with him, the deals they offered always put Carter at a disadvantage. He refused to sign their contracts and waited for a bigger and better opportunity.

Eventually, Jay-Z and his friend Damon Dash decided to form their own label, Roc-A-Fella Records. They tried for a long time and were finally able to get radio DJ Funkmaster Flex to play one of their songs, "Dead Presidents." Listeners loved it, and Jay-Z's career took off. His very first album, *Reasonable Doubt*, even went platinum, selling over two-and-a-quarter million copies. Enormous successes would **ensue** for many years. He released 18 albums, was the first hip-hop artist inducted into the Songwriters Hall of Fame, and became the record holder for having the most Number One albums by a solo artist on the *Billboard* 100.

As much as Jay-Z loved being in the spotlight, he didn't want everyone's expectations of him to **retard** his growth as an artist and a person. He stopped writing songs and became the head of the famous Def Jam Recordings. Because he had been a rapper, he had great **insight** into the problems artists face. Eventually, though, he decided to leave Def Jam and expand his own Roc-A-Fella label to form Roc Nation, which not only signs artists, but also organizes concerts and supports athletes. Fans might be familiar with one of Jay-Z's protégés: an artist named Kanye West! Another one of the multi-talented millionaire's companies, Rocawear, produces everything from designer clothing to wristwatches and cologne. What will he do next? It is both **plausible** and likely that Jay-Z isn't finished taking over the industry.

To say that Jay-Z is merely a successful rapper would be a great understatement. He has completely dominated the world of hip-hop in more ways than one. His **progression** from a lesser-known artist to a record company executive is certainly impressive. Although it may sound arrogant and **haughty**, Jay-Z speaks the truth when he says, "I'm not a businessman. I'm a business, man."

EXERCISE 1 / WORD LIST

Use the context in which the word is used to determine what the word probably means. Write a brief definition in the space provided.

1. **alacrity:** _____

   He also developed a love of words and read the dictionary with eagerness and **alacrity**.

2. **embezzle:** _____

   His friends warned him about the guile and greed of record companies, many of which **embezzle** money and have no concern for the artists' well-being.

3. **ensue:** _____

   His very first album, *Reasonable Doubt*, even went platinum, selling over two-and-a-quarter million copies. Enormous successes would **ensue** for many years.

4. **guile:** _____

   His friends warned him about the **guile** and greed of record companies, many of which embezzle money and have no concern for the artists' well-being.

5. **haughty:** _____

   Although it may sound arrogant and **haughty**, Jay-Z speaks the truth when he says, "I'm not a businessman. I'm a business, man."

6. **insight:** _____

   Because he had been a rapper, he had great **insight** into the problems artists face.

7. **manipulate:** _____

   Like other hip-hop artists, he knew it was essential to develop a large vocabulary that could be later **manipulated** to make rhymes.

8. **negotiate:** _____

   Although several company executives tried to **negotiate** with him, the deals they offered always put Carter at a disadvantage.

9. **plausible:** _____

It is both **plausible** and likely that Jay-Z isn't finished taking over the industry.

10. **progression:** _____

His **progression** from a lesser-known artist to a record company executive is certainly impressive.

11. **retard:** _____

As much as Jay-Z loved being in the spotlight, he didn't want everyone's expectations of him to **retard** his growth as an artist and a person.

EXERCISE 2 / USING WORDS IN CONTEXT

Fill in the blank with the vocabulary word that best completes the sentence. In some cases, you may need to change the tense or form of a verb or the number of a noun.

negotiate	guile	alacrity	insight	embezzle	progression
retard	ensue	haughty	plausible	manipulate	

1. Since there were tools on the dining room table, it is _____ that maintenance was going on in the apartment.

2. Once it began, the hostility known as the East Coast/West Coast rivalry _____ for decades.

3. The Union Army attempted to _____ the advancement of Confederate soldiers by putting land mines in the ground.

4. In the song "Star Power," Curren$y samples and _____ a song from Super Mario Bros. to fit his rap.

5. That book gives some _____ into the work conditions in a 19ᵗʰ-century textile mill.

6. It is easy to see Will Smith's _____ from a hip-hop artist to a movie star.

7. The fan ran onto the stage with great _____, eager to perform with his idol, Dr. Dre.

8. The two video editors tried to _____ a way to divide up the work.

9. Jay-Z used deception and _____ to get the rights to "Hard Knock Life" for one of his songs.

10. The corrupt president of the charity was arrested for _____ money that should have gone to people in need.

11. The girl usually exhibited a(n) _____ attitude because her family was the wealthiest in the area.

EXERCISE 3 / READING COMPREHENSION AND ANALYSIS

Select the best answers to the following questions based on a close and thorough reading of "Jay-Z."

1. The tone in the introductory paragraph can be best described as

    A. speculative.

    B. sarcastic.

    C. humorous.

    D. depressed.

    E. uplifting.

2. What trained Carter to memorize lyrics?

    A. He learned he could memorize words if he put them to song.

    B. He refused to bring his notebook into the recording studio.

    C. He memorized complete albums by many popular artists.

    D. He didn't have money to spend on paper and writing materials.

    E. He sometimes didn't have his notebook and had to wait to write lyrics down.

3. The phrase "weren't particularly fond" is an example of

    A. alliteration.

    B. allusion.

    C. understatement.

    D. metaphor.

    E. hyperbole.

4. The writer wants to add the following sentence to the passage. Choose the best paragraph in which to place it.

   "Jay-Z didn't want to feel pressured into releasing an album every year."

   A. Paragraph 2

   B. Paragraph 3

   C. Paragraph 4

   D. Paragraph 5

   E. Paragraph 6

5. With which statement would the writer most likely DISAGREE?

   A. All record labels take advantage of the artists they sign.

   B. Jay-Z helped and mentored Kanye West.

   C. A person can be both a successful businessman and a rapper.

   D. DJ Funkmaster Flex helped start Jay-Z's career.

   E. Jay-Z deserved to be inducted into the Songwriters Hall of Fame.

EXERCISE 4 / MAKING INFERENCES

Choose the best answer.

1. What can be inferred as the best reason Jay-Z created Roc-A-Fella?

   A. He was so offended by the other record labels that he wanted to outcompete them.

   B. He knew he could market his album and sell two-and-a-quarter million copies.

   C. He was being offered bad record deals and wanted to take control of his future.

   D. He wanted to convince DJ Funkmaster Flex that he was going to be famous.

2. Which of the following is NOT a correct example of how to use the word **insight**?

   A. Our family heirlooms gave us some insight into how our ancestors lived.

   B. The art exhibit gave us a fresh new insight into Rembrandt's inspiration.

   C. The closing of the school's library will probably insight a riot.

   D. The radiographs will allow the doctor to have greater insight into the illness.

3. If a woman always plays the piano with **alacrity**, she would probably NOT

   A. miss piano lessons.

   B. practice every day.

   C. study different musical periods.

   D. compose her own music.

4. A car mechanic with a great amount of **guile** might do which of the following?

   A. close the shop in the middle of a blizzard

   B. ask you to fill out a lot of paper work

   C. miss your call while talking to another customer

   D. sell poor-quality tires for more than what they're worth

5. Which of the following is NOT an example of **progression**?

   A. a person entering old age

   B. a married man thinking about his wedding day

   C. a book flowing from beginning to end

   D. a caterpillar turning into a butterfly

EXERCISE 5 / ROOTS, PREFIXES, AND SUFFIXES

Answer the questions below that are designed to help you arrive at some conclusions about word families and origins.

Roots: *gress,* "to go"
      manu/man, "hand"
      tard, "slow"

1. Based on the meaning of the *manu/man* root, answer the question that follows the sentence.

   The clanking of iron *manacles* signaled that a line of captives was being marched through town.

   Where were the captives' chains placed? _____

2. Use your knowledge of the *gress* root and the context of the sentence to define each italicized word below:

   A. Justin didn't know the letter he lost was important, but Brooke considered it a major *transgression.*

   _____

   B. The panelists tended to *digress* unless someone reminded them what the question had been.

   _____

   C. After her brother was born, Emma started to *regress* to childish behavior in order to get more of her parents' attention.

   _____

   D. The cobra didn't seem *aggressive,* but when a rat was put into the cage, the snake immediately attacked it.

   _____

3. Fire *accelerant* is the opposite of fire *retardant.* What does fire *accelerant* do?

   _____

4. Use the root that means "hand" to create words that fill in the blanks of the following sentences:

   A. Abby turned in her _____ to the publisher.

   B. At its peak, the assembly line could _____ one thousand bottles of root beer an hour.

   C. The problem with the computer was complicated and had to be repaired _____, which took all day.

FEMALE RAPPERS

A DISCUSSION OF hip-hop would be incomplete without mentioning contributions by female artists. Initially, the industry was largely dominated by men, who **alienated** female emcees and made them feel unwelcome in the world of rap. Several important women, however, broadened the scope of hip-hop by including their unique female narratives and perspectives.

One of the first female rappers was Sharon Green, who went by the name "Sha-Rock." She performed at some of DJ Kool Herc's parties and even engaged many experienced male emcees in rap battles. (You may recall that DJ Kool Herc was the creator of hip-hop.) She later joined the group Funky 4+1, but only as what some would consider a **subordinate**. She was the only female in the crew, an **adjunct** artist, the +1 in the name. Funky 4+1 became famous and was the first rap group to perform on *Saturday Night Live*. Coincidentally, they switched from the Enjoy record label to Sugar Hill Records, which had been cofounded by a *woman*: Sylvia Robinson. Even though Sha-Rock was the first female emcee, the first crew with all female members was actually Mercedes Ladies, which originated in the South Bronx in 1976. They are not as well known, but Mercedes Ladies also paved the way for many female groups.

One of the biggest moments in the history of women's rap occurred in 1984. UTFO, or Untouchable Force Organization, a group of male rappers, released a song entitled "Roxanne, Roxanne." In the rap, fictional versions of the group members flirt with a woman named Roxanne. She turns down their advances. Offended, they insult her, calling her "stuck up," and making cruel remarks about her family. Many female fans and artists felt the song was an **affront** to women; however, it presented an opportunity for the then-unknown rapper Roxanne Shanté. Although she wasn't the Roxanne referenced in the rap, she **lampooned** UTFO, making fun of their misogynistic views. Other female rappers did

the same. This back-and-forth soon became known as "The Roxanne Wars."

Many more female rappers began to emerge in the hip-hop world around the late 1980s. MC Lyte, for example, became the first female rapper to release a solo album. Additionally, her single "Paper Thin" sold over 125,000 copies, despite the fact that it was played on the radio infrequently. The rap was about one of MC Lyte's cheating ex-boyfriends. The topic of infidelity is actually very common in the music of female rappers, who **reprimand** men for focusing on women's bodies and not respecting them as actual people. Female artists also speak out against chauvinism and domestic violence. They express themselves in their own way, giving them the freedom to choose the image that they project and use it as a form of empowerment. This sometimes includes **narcissistic** bragging, as well as clothing and dancing that might be considered licentious. Like male artists, they also boast about their legitimacy or "street cred."

That isn't to say, however, that there is hostility between male and female artists. While several women promoted themselves independently, just as MC Lyte did, some were supported by famous male rappers or groups. For example, Public Enemy promoted Sister Souljah, and P. Diddy helped Mary J. Blige. Both women have had successful careers based on their talent, not because of the men that they associated with.

Although female and male rap artists often discuss the same topics—such as guns, drugs, violence, gangs, and life in the inner city—the **articulate** female artists voice issues that are unique to women's experiences. Hip-hop is now more **inclusive**, and the number of women artists has expanded. Respect should be given to the **emissaries**, the ambassadors, the pioneers who inspired and motivated generations of female rappers.

EXERCISE 1 / WORD LIST

Use the context in which the word is used to determine what the word probably means. Write a brief definition in the space provided.

1. **adjunct:** _____

   She later joined the group Funky 4+1, but only as what some would consider a subordinate. She was the only female in the crew, an **adjunct** artist, the +1 in the name.

2. **affront:** _____

   Offended, they insult her, calling her "stuck up," and making cruel remarks about her family. Many female fans and artists felt the song was an **affront** to women; however, it presented an opportunity for the then-unknown rapper Roxanne Shanté.

3. **alienate:** _____

   Initially, the industry was largely dominated by men, who **alienated** female emcees and made them feel unwelcome in the world of rap.

4. **articulate:** _____

   Although female and male rap artists often discuss the same topics—such as guns, drugs, violence, gangs, and life in the inner city—the **articulate** female artists voice issues that are unique to women's experiences.

5. **emissary:** _____

   Respect should be given to the **emissaries**, the ambassadors, the pioneers who inspired and motivated generations of female rappers.

6. **inclusive:** _____

   Hip-hop is now more **inclusive**, and the number of women artists has expanded.

7. **lampoon:** _____

   Although she wasn't the Roxanne referenced in the rap, she **lampooned** UTFO, making fun of their misogynistic views.

8. **narcissistic:** _____

They express themselves in their own way, giving them the freedom to choose the image that they project and use it as a form of empowerment. This sometimes includes **narcissistic** bragging, as well as clothing and dancing that might be considered licentious.

9. **reprimand:** _____

The topic of infidelity is actually very common in the music of female rappers, who **reprimand** men for focusing on women's bodies and not respecting them as actual people.

10. **subordinate:** _____

She later joined the group Funky 4+1, but only as what some would consider a **subordinate**. She was the only female in the crew, an adjunct artist, the +1 in the name.

EXERCISE 2 / USING WORDS IN CONTEXT

Fill in the blank with the vocabulary word that best completes the sentence. In some cases, you may need to change the tense or form of a verb or the number of a noun.

lampoon	affront	inclusive	adjunct	narcissistic
reprimand	alienate	articulate	emissary	subordinate

1. I must not have been _____ enough when I gave the instructions because everyone did the opposite of what I said.

2. N.W.A considered it a huge _____ when Ice Cube left the group to start a solo career.

3. They didn't want to _____ Chris, but he just wasn't good enough to make the chess team.

4. Monica got a stern _____ from her mother when she was late coming home from the school dance.

5. Music critics, and even her own fans, viewed Nicki Minaj as _____ when she claimed to be the Queen of Rap.

6. Satire Rap is a new genre that parodies and _____ other forms of rap in a funny way.

7. The scouts sent a(n) _____ to the captain to report where the enemy troops were located.

8. The college needed a(n) _____ computer expert to teach coding part time this summer.

9. The school's Shakespeare group was _____, consisting of people of all different ages and years of experience.

10. The boss had eight different _____ with various areas of expertise who advised him on key issues.

EXERCISE 3 / READING COMPREHENSION AND ANALYSIS

Select the best answers to the following questions based on a close and thorough reading of "Female Rappers."

1. The primary purpose of the passage is to

    A. condemn male artists for making the hip-hop industry hostile to women.

    B. provide biographical information on a few female artists.

    C. encourage women to become female rappers.

    D. highlight the contribution of female rappers.

    E. express anger that it has taken a long time for women to be recognized.

2. What about being +1 in the Funky 4+1 would make Sha-Rock seem to be an **adjunct** member?

    A. The +1 was often accidentally dropped from the name.

    B. The men refused to include her in concerts.

    C. She was not the only female in the group.

    D. She wasn't allowed to rap about issues important to her.

    E. The +1 indicates that she was not considered part of the group.

3. What is the best reason the word *woman* is italicized in Paragraph 2?

    A. It makes the reader question whether Sylvia Robinson created the group.

    B. It contributes to the topic of important women in the hip-hop industry.

    C. It hints at the initial resistance to having a woman start a record label.

    D. It suggests that it was actually Robinson's husband who started the label.

    E. It directly insults Sylvia Robinson for her success in the music industry.

4. Read the following quotation from "The Roots of Rap":

    "Living in a dangerous urban area makes an artist seem more legitimate, proving that he or she has survived in a difficult environment and understands the problems faced on the streets. Because of this, many rappers mention the cities in which they live, and some even praise the violent crime there."

    Based on this quotation, what would female rappers "boast about" to give them the "street cred" that is mentioned in Paragraph 4 of this passage?

    A. living in a dangerous area

    B. how attractive they are

    C. owning expensive things

    D. an ability to dance well

    E. escaping their neighborhoods

5. The last paragraph mentions "issues that are unique to women's experiences." What is NOT an issue discussed in this passage?

    A. Women are too reluctant to attack men in their raps.

    B. Women often have to deal with cheating boyfriends.

    C. Women are sometimes respected more for their looks than for their minds.

    D. Male artists in a rap group with females give them a secondary role.

    E. Female artists can portray themselves in ways that empower them.

EXERCISE 4 / MAKING INFERENCES

Choose the best answer.

1. Which of the following would LEAST likely be an **inclusive** group?

    A. a volleyball team in a community center

    B. a country club for the wealthy

    C. a game of basketball in a park

    D. a concert that is free to attend

2. Someone **lampooning** a rival football team might

    A. draw a cartoon making the school's mascot look ridiculous.

    B. list the number of games the team lost in the last five years.

    C. call the other team's coach on the phone repeatedly.

    D. accuse the team's quarterback of being a sore loser.

3. Which would NOT fit the definition of **adjunct**?

    A. a football player who plays only at home games

    B. a grammar workshop that takes place after English class

    C. a special diet in addition to medication for a disease

    D. a part required to make a car's engine work

4. Of the following people, who would be the best example of an **emissary**?

    A. a door-to-door salesperson for a company

    B. a dean of a university speaking at a high school

    C. a veterinarian in a large animal hospital

    D. a famous actor talking about his career

5. In Paragraph 4, what would most likely be the reason MC Lyte's "Paper Thin" was not being played on the radio?

    A. "Paper Thin" did not appeal to the audience.

    B. The song included vulgar and controversial lyrics.

    C. "Paper Thin" was a poorly written rap song.

    D. Radio stations were reluctant to play rap written by a woman.

EXERCISE 5 / ROOTS, PREFIXES, AND SUFFIXES

Answer the questions below that are designed to help you arrive at some conclusions about word families and origins.

1. We use the word **narcissistic** in the passage. Even though it doesn't come from a root that you're familiar with, it comes directly from a character in Greek mythology named *Narcissus*.

    Which of the following describes *narcissists*?

    A. people who change their minds frequently

    B. people who have only one weakness

    C. people who are in love with themselves

    D. people who possess amazing strength

2. The roots *mit* and *mis* mean "to send." List as many words as you can that use the root *mit* or *mis*. Use a dictionary if necessary.

    _____

    _____

3. Use the following prefixes and root to come up with the word in each blank.

Prefixes	Root
se–, "away"	*clud*, "to close"
ex–, "out"	
pre–, "before"	

    A. _____ = "to leave out"

    B. _____ = "to close off beforehand," "to prevent"

    C. _____ = "closed off from people," "private"

THE QUEEN

SEXISM IN HIP-HOP is **prevalent**, with many male rappers sexualizing and degrading women. Yet, some artists work to counter that treatment with positive portrayals of females. Queen Latifah, in particular, empowers women through her music. In the late 1980s, Latifah defied common ideas about rap artists and uplifted women in her songs. She was **idolized** by girls who viewed her as an inspiration.

Queen Latifah was born Dana Owens on March 18, 1970. "Latifah" is an Arabic word that means "delicate" or "sensitive"; she added the "Queen" herself. Her interest in music started at a young age, and she sang in her church choir and performed as Dorothy in the musical *The Wiz* at St. Anne's parochial school. In high school, she formed the rap group Ladies Fresh with two friends. Her mother tried to popularize the group and invited DJ Mark James to hear their music; James, in turn, brought a demo tape of Queen Latifah to Tommy Boy Records, and she signed to that label. Latifah's first single, "Wrath of My Madness," showed her self-pride and **aplomb** as she proclaimed herself the "new Queen" and believed in "the woman inside of [her]." Her following album, *All Hail the Queen*, proved that she was a talented, **respectable** hip-hop artist.

In a hit song from *All Hail the Queen*, "Ladies First," Owens challenged the messages and attitudes of male rappers. Yet, she remained **eloquent** and civil, **alluding** to the problems of hip-hop culture rather than calling them out directly. Although rap music videos often showed women **gyrating** their hips in revealing clothes, the video for "Ladies First" did not include anything suggestive. Instead, Latifah portrayed black women as powerful and historically important by paying homage to Harriet Tubman, Sojourner Truth, Angela Davis, and Winnie Mandela. With this tribute, Owens and accompanying rapper Monie Love illustrated black women's civil rights activism. Queen Latifah, who calls herself "a proud, black woman," not a feminist, spoke about women and political causes; music critics and fans loved her **righteous** message. *All Hail the Queen* soon climbed to the top ten on R&B charts.

Latifah's second album, *Nature of a Sista*, sold fewer copies than her first, and Owens's career hit its **nadir** when Tommy Boy Records did not renew her contract. Then, less than a year later, she suffered a personal tragedy: Her brother died in a motorcycle accident. Despite Latifah's grief, she **persevered** and worked hard on her music. She signed with Motown Records and released her third album in 1993. This album, *Black Reign*, sold half a million copies in the United States and included her most popular single, "U.N.I.T.Y." In this hit song, Latifah declared that she will not **tolerate** negativity about women—whether it's insulting comments, harassment, or domestic abuse—and she insisted that men treat women with proper respect. "U.N.I.T.Y.," probably her most **memorable** song, earned her a Grammy for Best Solo Rap Performance.

After receiving the award, Queen Latifah took a five-year break from music. During this time, she acted and expanded her entertainment career. She starred in movies and made appearances on TV. In 1998, however, Latifah released *Order in the Court*. On her next two albums, Owens showcased her vast musical talent by performing jazz. She returned to rap in 2009 with *Persona*, working with Missy Elliott, Mary J. Blige, and other hip-hop artists. As her collaboration with female rappers suggests, Queen Latifah continues to support women and encourage young girls, while consistently remaining true to the values she considers important.

EXERCISE 1 / WORD LIST

Use the context in which the word is used to determine what the word probably means. Write a brief definition in the space provided.

1. **allude:** _____

   Yet, she remained eloquent and civil, **alluding** to the problems of hip-hop culture rather than calling them out directly.

2. **aplomb:** _____

   Latifah's first single, "Wrath of My Madness," showed her self-pride and **aplomb** as she proclaimed herself the "new Queen" and believed in "the woman inside of [her]."

3. **eloquent:** _____

   Yet, she remained **eloquent** and civil, alluding to the problems of hip-hop culture rather than calling them out directly.

4. **gyrate:** _____

   Although rap music videos often showed women **gyrating** their hips in revealing clothes, the video for "Ladies First" did not include anything suggestive.

5. **idolize:** _____

   She was **idolized** by girls who viewed her as an inspiration.

6. **memorable:** _____

   "U.N.I.T.Y.," probably her most **memorable** song, earned her a Grammy for Best Solo Rap Performance.

7. **nadir:** _____

   Latifah's second album, *Nature of a Sista*, sold fewer copies than her first, and Owens's career hit its **nadir** when Tommy Boy Records did not renew her contract.

8. **persevere:** _____

   Despite Latifah's grief, she **persevered** and worked hard on her music.

9. **prevalent:** _____

   Sexism in hip-hop is **prevalent**, with many male rappers sexualizing and degrading women.

10. **respectable:** _____

    Her following album, *All Hail the Queen*, proved that she was a talented, **respectable** hip-hop artist.

11. **righteous:** _____

    Queen Latifah, who calls herself "a proud, black woman," not a feminist, spoke about women and political causes; music critics and fans loved her **righteous** message.

12. **tolerate:** _____

    In this hit song, Latifah declared that she will not **tolerate** negativity about women—whether it's insulting comments, harassment, or domestic abuse…

EXERCISE 2 / USING WORDS IN CONTEXT

Fill in the blank with the vocabulary word that best completes the sentence. In some cases, you may need to change the tense or form of a verb or the number of a noun.

tolerate	aplomb	gyrate	eloquent	persevere	nadir
memorable	prevalent	idolize	righteous	respectable	allude

1. Many early songs by Queen Latifah didn't just _____ to the mistreatment of women—they condemned it.

2. People frequently feel that hip-hop simply uses the language of the streets and do not realize that many songs are quite _____.

3. Even though she was the new student in the class, Stephanie showed great _____ when she delivered her first speech.

4. A(n) _____ belief in gangsta rap is that nothing else in life is as important as girls, violence, and money.

5. The most _____ time of Lawrence's entire vacation was when he caught a fish that weighed more than 150 pounds.

6. My grandmother says she cannot _____ my music; I don't like her choices in music, either.

7. It's important not to _____ famous people because they are not perfect and can easily disappoint their fans.

8. If Public Enemy hadn't _____ and remained committed to their music when their first record didn't sell many copies, they might not have made a second one.

9. The music promoter said, "We don't just want a(n) _____-looking group on stage. What we want is a group that looks good, but has an inner-city feel to it."

10. Few sayings are as simple or as _____ as "Do unto others as you would have them do unto you."

11. The _____ of the disastrous concert happened when the lead singer forgot the lyrics to the band's most famous song.

12. As the strong winds began to _____ and form a tornado, my family and I gathered some supplies and ran to our basement.

EXERCISE 3 / READING COMPREHENSION AND ANALYSIS

Select the best answers to the following questions based on a close and thorough reading of "The Queen."

1. According to the passage, why did Queen Latifah take a break from recording?

    A. Tommy Boy Records failed to renew her contract.

    B. She was tired of the work and needed some free time.

    C. She did not appreciate being called a feminist.

    D. Latifah wanted to expand the limits of her career.

    E. "U.N.I.T.Y." was not treated with the proper respect.

2. The main idea of this passage is that Queen Latifah

    A. stands up for women's rights.

    B. is the writer of the song "U.N.I.T.Y."

    C. is a great female rapper.

    D. doesn't like the term "feminist."

    E. is the first female rap star.

3. What is the name of Queen Latifah's first single?

   A. *Order in the Court*

   B. "U.N.I.T.Y."

   C. *All Hail the Queen*

   D. "Ladies First"

   E. "Wrath of My Madness"

4. The word *however* in the last paragraph is a signal that the reader should expect

   A. an entirely new topic.

   B. an explanation of the topic.

   C. a different opinion on the topic.

   D. a change within the topic.

   E. a conclusion of the topic.

5. In the sentence "With this tribute, Owens and accompanying rapper Monie Love illustrated black women's civil rights activism," which phrase can best be substituted for the word *illustrated*? Other facts in the paragraph will help you decide.

   A. made a painting on the cover of

   B. showed their own support for

   C. reworked an old approach to

   D. proved that America believed in

   E. pointed out the power of

EXERCISE 4 / MAKING INFERENCES

Choose the best answer.

1. If something is **memorable**, it probably

   A. has a strong memory.

   B. has a weak memory.

   C. can't be forgotten.

   D. is difficult to remember.

2. All of the following statements can be logically inferred from the passage EXCEPT

   A. Queen Latifah enjoyed making music with other artists.

   B. Latifah never would have succeeded if she hadn't signed with Tommy Boy.

   C. Dana Owens changed her name to "Latifah" to express how she felt about herself.

   D. Queen Latifah's music has a strong appeal to many people.

3. Which of the following is the weakest example of the use of the word **persevere**?

   A. installing batteries in a flashlight

   B. studying for final exams in math and English

   C. working on a research paper to get it perfect

   D. driving 50 miles in the snow to get home

4. Which one of these could best be described as **prevalent**?

   A. car races

   B. smartphones

   C. rare books

   D. drones

5. All the following quotations show a use of the word **allude** EXCEPT

   A. "I wonder why he mentioned 'The Raven,' that poem by Edgar Allan Poe."

   B. "Everyone, even kids who are only in third grade, knows who Honest Abe is."

   C. "I love to play basketball because I can dunk better than anybody else."

   D. "Mike thinks he can rap, but after I heard him, I knew he was no Tupac."

EXERCISE 5 / ROOTS, PREFIXES, AND SUFFIXES

Answer the questions below that are designed to help you arrive at some conclusions about word families and origins.

Roots: *loq, locut,* "to speak"
      lud/lus, "to play"

1. The suffix *–ous* means "full of."

    Naomi needed some quiet time after the morning with her *loquacious* brother.

    Based on the root *loq,* the suffix, and the sentence, what does *loquacious* mean?

    _____

2. The word *collude* means "to plot together."

    The court found that the two men had *colluded* to rob the bank.

    James and Alia *colluded* to trick their teacher.

    What might the prefix *con–* mean in the word *collude*?

    _____

3. Based on your knowledge of roots, fill in the root for each of the following words:

    e _____ uent = speaking beautifully

    _____ icrous = silly, ridiculous

    col _____ quial = conversational

    de _____ e = to trick

SLIM SHADY

WILL THE REAL Slim Shady please stand up?

Regardless of whether you adore or **abhor** him, Eminem is in your face. Whether he's running around dressed as a superhero or **impersonating** a pop star, you can depend on him to shock and entertain. But before the birth of the over-the-top Slim Shady persona, Marshall Mathers was a shy boy, hardened by the **callous** and cold-hearted neighborhoods of Detroit.

Marshall Mathers, III, or "Eminem," was born on October 17, 1972. When he was young, he and his mother relocated from St. Joseph, Missouri, to Detroit, Michigan, where they moved between different apartments and shelters. Because he frequently changed schools—and was also one of the few white children in a predominantly black community—Mathers was constantly bullied. On one occasion, another student beat him up so badly that he was in a coma for over a week. His mistrust of others made him **aloof** and distant, so he began to spend more time alone, focusing on music. He was inspired by hip-hop groups like Public Enemy and N.W.A, and he and his Uncle Ronnie, who was around the same age, wrote and listened to rap in their basement. Although he dropped out of school in 9th grade, Mathers had an obsession with language. In an interview, he said the following:

"I found that no matter how bad I was at school…and no matter how low my grades might have been at some times, I always was good at English.…I just felt like I wanna be able to have all of these words at my disposal, in my vocabulary at all times, whenever I need to pull 'em out."

While working part-time jobs, Mathers began recording. He sent one of his EPs, *Infinite*, to radio stations, and he participated in local rap battles. Despite his talent and **laborious** efforts, nobody was interested in his music. However, rather than be defeated by the disappointing **ordeal** of being constantly rejected, he followed advice he later put into his song called "Lose Yourself":

"Look, if you had one shot, or one opportunity, to seize everything you ever wanted, in one moment, would you capture it, or just let it slip?"

Mathers did not "let it slip," and while failure initially made him depressed and **pessimistic**, he began to voice his frustration through the persona he invented, Slim Shady. He wrote and recorded the *Slim Shady EP*, and he challenged other rappers in freestyle battles at the 1997 Rap Olympics in Los Angeles. Even though he competed against more experienced artists, he won 2nd place. Dr. Dre, a producer and former member of N.W.A, heard some of the music and was so impressed that he signed Mathers to his label, Aftermath Records. After recording the *Slim Shady LP*, the first single, "My Name Is," reached Number 10 on the *Billboard* 200 chart. It wasn't just **momentary** success for Mathers, though, because his fame has lasted for more than two decades. He has released at least eight albums, six of which won Grammys for Best Rap Album. Two of his albums even achieved Diamond status: *The Eminem Show* and *The Marshall Mathers LP*. Mathers has been in the media spotlight ever since he first became a star.

Who would have thought a quiet **introvert** could become one of the most famous rappers in history! No one can deny Eminem's talent, yet some critics object to Slim Shady's antics and his lyrics that promote **decadence** and immoral behavior. To this, Mathers responds, "I say what I want to say and do what I want to do. There's no in-between. People will either love you for it or hate you for it."

EXERCISE 1 / WORD LIST

Use the context in which the word is used to determine what the word probably means. Write a brief definition in the space provided.

1. **abhor:** _____

Regardless of whether you adore or **abhor** him, Eminem is in your face.

2. **aloof:** _____

His mistrust of others made him **aloof** and distant, so he began to spend more time alone, focusing on music.

3. **callous:** _____

But before the birth of the over-the-top Slim Shady persona, Marshall Mathers was a shy boy, hardened by the **callous** and cold-hearted neighborhoods of Detroit.

4. **decadence:** _____

No one can deny Eminem's talent, yet some critics object to Slim Shady's antics and his lyrics that promote **decadence** and immoral behavior.

5. **impersonate:** _____

Whether he's running around dressed as a superhero or **impersonating** a pop star, you can depend on him to shock and entertain.

6. **introvert:** _____

Who would have thought a quiet **introvert** could become one of the most famous rappers in history!

7. **laborious:** _____

Despite his talent and **laborious** efforts, nobody was interested in his music.

8. **momentary:** _____

It wasn't just **momentary** success for Mathers, though, because his fame has lasted for more than two decades.

9. **ordeal:** _____

However, rather than be defeated by the disappointing **ordeal** of being constantly rejected, he followed advice he later put into his song called "Lose Yourself"...

10. **pessimistic:** _____

Mathers did not "let it slip," and while failure initially made him depressed and **pessimistic**, he began to voice his frustration through the persona he invented, Slim Shady.

EXERCISE 2 / USING WORDS IN CONTEXT

Fill in the blank with the vocabulary word that best completes the sentence. In some cases, you may need to change the tense or form of a verb or the number of a noun.

decadence	momentary	aloof	introvert	impersonate
abhor	callous	ordeal	laborious	pessimistic

1. Emily tends to be a(n) _____ and prefers listening to music at home rather than going to concerts.

2. Even though some rap lyrics reveal a(n) _____ view of the world, some songs are hopeful and express positive aspects of life.

3. Although the group did not stay together for long, The Fugees had a(n) _____ reunion in 2006.

4. Becoming established as an artist and businessman was a long and _____ process for Jay-Z.

5. It was very _____ of our next-door neighbor to ignore the request of the community to remove the broken-down car from in front of his house.

6. One of the things many hip-hop artists _____ is how the media invades their personal lives.

7. Eva's friends grew worried because she seemed very _____ during class, but it turned out that she just had not been feeling well.

8. Many fans think Shad Moss _____ 50 Cent really well and captures the artist's mannerisms perfectly.

9. When the argument broke out between my friends, I tried to stay out of the whole
   _____ and refused to get involved.

10. In Oscar Wilde's novel, Dorian Gray's moral _____, selfish behavior, and lack of
    concern for anyone other than himself eventually leads to his ruin.

EXERCISE 3 / READING COMPREHENSION AND ANALYSIS

Select the best answers to the following questions based on a close and thorough reading of "Slim Shady."

1. This passage is organized by

   A. topic.

   B. chronology.

   C. point and counterpoint.

   D. question and answer.

   E. importance.

2. The first sentence in the passage is a line from Mathers's song "The Real Slim Shady." What
   purpose does this reference serve in the text?

   A. It introduces the topic of his various identities.

   B. It demonstrates his songwriting abilities.

   C. It implies that he is not what he appears to be.

   D. It shows how he is unique as a rapper.

   E. It suggests that his persona is more important than he is.

3. Which is the best paraphrase of the following sentence?

   "Mathers did not 'let it [opportunity] slip,' and while failure initially made him depressed and
   pessimistic, he began to voice his frustration through the persona he invented, Slim Shady."

   A. Mathers refused to give up, and he used Slim Shady to express his negative feelings.

   B. Mathers invented Slim Shady to express his mistrust of people in the industry.

   C. Mathers ignored his sadness, frustration, and pessimism by creating Slim Shady.

   D. Mathers did not slip in his determination to allow Slim Shady to say what he felt.

   E. Mathers failed at first, but his stage character, Slim Shady, did not.

4. Which of the following did NOT happen to Mathers in his childhood?

    A. He dropped out of high school.

    B. He lived in multiple places in Detroit, Michigan.

    C. He attended several schools.

    D. He wrote music with his Uncle Ronnie.

    E. He became famous for his freestyling abilities.

5. Compare the Jay-Z and Eminem passages. Which of the following do the two artists have in common?

    A. They were able to memorize lyrics and didn't have to write them down.

    B. They studied words and developed large vocabularies to use in their raps.

    C. They both were very reluctant to enter into the music industry.

    D. They both created stage personas that would eventually annoy the critics.

    E. They are both businessmen in addition to being successful rappers.

EXERCISE 4 / MAKING INFERENCES

Choose the best answer.

1. What is something a person with a **pessimistic** attitude might say?

    A. "The statistics about animal abuse are wrong."

    B. "The moon landing is a hoax created by the government."

    C. "We can never achieve world peace."

    D. "Nobody has ever seen the Loch Ness Monster."

2. Which is the best reason there might be a **momentary** increase in chocolate sales?

    A. There are more chocolate factories.

    B. Valentine's Day is coming.

    C. The cost of buying chocolate will continue to fall.

    D. Children are eating more chocolate than they did in the past.

3. Which of the following is NOT an example of something earned through **laborious** work?

    A. a college degree in a difficult subject

    B. the inheritance of a large amount of money

    C. coming in 1st in the 100m dash

    D. the start of a landscaping business

4. Which is an activity an **introvert** would probably NOT enjoy?

    A. playing a video game

    B. dancing at a school event

    C. reading an anthology of poetry

    D. planting a vegetable garden

5. What can be inferred is the primary reason Mathers was bullied at school?

    A. He was frequently the new kid no one knew.

    B. He did not want to interact with the other kids.

    C. He boasted about his freestyling abilities.

    D. He didn't care about getting good grades.

EXERCISE 5 / ROOTS, PREFIXES, AND SUFFIXES

Answer the questions below that are designed to help you arrive at some conclusions about word families and origins.

Roots: *hor*, "dread"
      labor, "toil, exertion"
      vert/vers, "to turn"

1. Using your knowledge of roots, pick the word that means the same as the underlined phrase.

   Dre and Katya decided they would <u>work together</u> on the next record.

   A. collaborate

   B. revert

   C. horrify

   D. convert

2. Based on the meaning of the *hor* root and its use in the sentence below, give a definition of the word *horrify*.

   Kim knew that nothing would *horrify* her mother more than the huge mess in the kitchen.

   _____

3. Read the following sentence and then write a definition for the italicized word.

   Jeremy said that the party had been a disaster, but he refused to *elaborate*.

   _____

4. Choose a root from this exercise to create a word that fits in the following sentence.

   A place where work or research is done is a _____.

5. Explain how we might get each of the following words from the root *vert/vers*.

   An *aversion* is a "dislike": She has an *aversion* to vegetables.

   _____

   A *diversion* is a distraction: The magician created a *diversion* so the audience would think the rabbit had disappeared.

   _____

   A *conversion* is a transformation: The *conversion* of water into steam took only a moment.

   _____

DOGG IN THE HOUSE

I WAS TEN YEARS old when *The Doggfather* came out. How my mom heard about the album still **eludes** me, but she said that I absolutely, under no circumstances, was allowed to listen to it. The funny thing was, I never asked! I had no interest in hip-hop; I was still completely **mesmerized** by Disney and prancing around the living room to "The Circle of Life." What did I care about Snoop Dogg? It wasn't until years later that I began to appreciate him, not only as a musician, but also as a celebrity.

Calvin Cordozar Broadus, Jr., was born on October 20, 1971, in Long Beach, California. His mother gave him the nickname "Snoop" supposedly after Snoopy in the Peanuts cartoons. Snoop has changed his name many times over the years. For example, he has been Snoop Dogg, Snoop Lion, and Snoopzilla. Back when he was a boy and known just as Snoop, however, he played the piano and sang in his church choir. Heavily interested in hip-hop, he and his friends Warren G and Nate Dogg formed the group 213, named after the Long Beach area code. One of their first tapes was of Snoop rapping over En Vogue's "Hold On." Dr. Dre, Warren G's famous stepbrother, heard it and invited Snoop to rap on "Deep Cover," a song featured in a movie of the same name. Snoop also made important contributions to Dre's album *The Chronic*, and, under Dre's guidance, he began a solo career. You could **attribute** Snoop's start to **nepotism** between Dr. Dre and Warren G., but his success was due to his verbal flow and the unique lyrical content of his songs. Rappers like Eminem, Jay-Z, and Tupac have mentioned in interviews that they studied the dictionary to develop large vocabularies; Snoop, on the other hand, created his own. *Doggystyle*, his first album, was the first debut album to enter the *Billboard* 200 chart at Number One. Personally, I'd like to imagine its success was due to parents' buying the album to assess its **morality** and decide how disgusted they should be. Snoop eventually released 15 studio albums and was featured on several more. Through the years, the musical style of his songs has varied. While most of his songs can be categorized as hip-hop, he has also written in other genres, even reggae and country!

Aside from being a successful musician, Snoop has become a pop culture icon. Easily recognizable by his laid-back attitude and dry sense of humor, he has made cameos in several movies, television shows, and music videos. One might even be **overwhelmed** by his numerous appearances. He has often been featured on *Jimmy Kimmel Live*, narrating segments of animal clips in a fake documentary appropriately named "Plizzanet Earth." He can also be seen on *Martha & Snoop's Potluck Dinner Party*, a cooking show on which Martha Stewart teaches Snoop and the audience how to make certain dishes. Of course, Snoop adds his own **culinary** flair. He makes amusing—but never **malicious**—jokes about other celebrities in *Comedy Central Roasts* and appears in parody videos like The Lonely Island's "Turtleneck and Chains." Snoop seems to be just about everywhere, in all forms of media.

As would probably be expected, my music tastes have evolved, incorporating a bit more of Snoop Dogg and a little less of *The Lion King*. I secretly wonder, given her expertise on the subject, whether my mom hasn't **feigned** disgust and been a secret fan of Snoop's for the last twenty years. Regardless, whatever discussion his music may have **provoked** at PTA meetings, he remains an important and entertaining member of the hip-hop world.

EXERCISE 1 / WORD LIST

Use the context in which the word is used to determine what the word probably means. Write a brief definition in the space provided.

1. **attribute:** _____

   You could **attribute** Snoop's start to nepotism between Dr. Dre and Warren G, but his success was due to his verbal flow and the unique lyrical content of his songs.

2. **culinary:** _____

   He can also be seen on *Martha & Snoop's Potluck Dinner Party*, a cooking show on which Martha Stewart teaches Snoop and the audience how to make certain dishes. Of course, Snoop adds his own **culinary** flair.

3. **elude:** _____

   How my mom heard about the album still **eludes** me, but she said that I absolutely, under no circumstances, was allowed to listen to it.

4. **feign:** _____

   I secretly wonder, given her expertise on the subject, whether my mom hasn't **feigned** disgust and been a secret fan of Snoop's for the last twenty years.

5. **malicious:** _____

   He makes amusing—but never **malicious**—jokes about other celebrities in *Comedy Central Roasts* and appears in parody videos like The Lonely Island's "Turtleneck and Chains."

6. **mesmerized:** _____

   The funny thing was, I never asked! I had no interest in hip-hop: I was still completely **mesmerized** by Disney and prancing around the living room to "The Circle of Life."

7. **morality:** _____

   Personally, I'd like to imagine its success was due to parents' buying the album to assess its **morality** and decide how disgusted they should be.

8. **nepotism:** _____

   You could attribute Snoop's start to **nepotism** between Dr. Dre and Warren G, but his success was due to his verbal flow and the unique lyrical content of his songs.

9. **overwhelmed:** _____

   Easily recognizable by his laid-back attitude and dry sense of humor, he has made cameos in several movies, television shows, and music videos. One might even be **overwhelmed** by his numerous appearances.

10. **provoke:** _____

   Regardless, whatever discussion his music may have **provoked** at PTA meetings, he remains an important and entertaining member of the hip-hop world.

EXERCISE 2 / USING WORDS IN CONTEXT

Fill in the blank with the vocabulary word that best completes the sentence. In some cases, you may need to change the tense or form of a verb or the number of a noun.

nepotism	morality	culinary	feign	overwhelmed
mesmerized	provoke	elude	attribute	malicious

1. You can _____ Lily's quick recovery to the excellent care she received at the veterinary hospital.

2. Although one would not suspect 2 Chainz of having _____ interests, he has written his own cookbook in which he offers musical selections to accompany his food.

3. A series of _____ tweets from Tyler the Creator to Chris Brown led to the creation of the phrase "Do You Like Soup?"

4. The assistant manager probably got his job because of _____; he has no qualifications and is the boss's nephew.

5. We were _____ by Twista's styling, which wasn't surprising since he was once known as the "Fastest Rapper Alive" and was capable of singing up to 11.2 syllables a second.

6. The bombing of Pearl Harbor _____ the United States to declare war on Japan and enter World War II.

7. Jess _____ interest in her boyfriend's poetry even though she thought it was overdramatic and ridiculous.

8. "Thieves in the Night" by Black Star references both the Bible and Toni Morrison's book *The Bluest Eye*, even though that fact _____ most listeners.

9. Most Public Enemy fans were _____ with disappointment when Flavor Flav became the star of his own silly reality show.

10. Michael's strong opinions about _____ and proper manners lead him to judge people unfairly.

EXERCISE 3 / READING COMPREHENSION AND ANALYSIS

Select the best answers to the following questions based on a close and thorough reading of "Dogg in the House."

1. Choose the best paraphrase of the following sentence:

   "You could attribute Snoop's start to nepotism between Dr. Dre and Warren G, but his success was due to his verbal flow and the unique lyrical content of his songs."

   A. Even though Snoop was related to Dr. Dre, he didn't use the connection to get his start in the music industry.

   B. The choice of words and the way they are used contribute greatly to a rapper's success.

   C. Snoop's success was due to his talent, not because he was connected to a famous rapper.

   D. Snoop was hired because of Warren G's relationship with Dr. Dre, and there are similarities among all three in their music and performances.

   E. Many people criticize Snoop and say that he wouldn't have become famous if Dr. Dre wasn't related to Warren G.

2. Which of the following statements can be inferred about the narrator?

   A. The narrator is a female.

   B. The narrator dislikes rap music.

   C. The narrator is around thirty years old.

   D. The narrator's mother was in the PTA.

   E. The narrator is a fan of The Lonely Island.

3. Based on the passage, which of the following statements is true?

   A. Snoop has appeared on many television shows.

   B. Snoop was inspired by Jay-Z, Eminem, and Tupac.

   C. Snoop's first rap was a tape of a song by En Vogue.

   D. *Doggystyle* was parodied on Comedy Central.

   E. *The Doggfather* was Snoop's first album.

4. What is the narrator's tone in the following sentence?

   "Personally, I'd like to imagine its success was due to parents' buying the album to assess its morality and decide how disgusted they should be."

   A. disappointed

   B. lighthearted

   C. concerned

   D. curious

   E. depressed

5. Which would be the best alternative title for this passage?

   A. What Ever Happened to 213?

   B. Dr. Dre's Famous Protégé

   C. Snoop Dogg: Musician and Celebrity

   D. Learn to Cook with Snoop Dogg

   E. Snoop Dogg: The Bane of Parents' Existence

EXERCISE 4 / MAKING INFERENCES

Choose the best answer.

1. Which of the following essays would likely contain a discussion of **morality**?

   A. "How a Workplace Dress Code Benefits Employees"

   B. "Is Stealing out of Necessity Truly a Crime?"

   C. "The Role of White Blood Cells in Inflammation"

   D. "The Shipping Industry's Effect on the Economy"

2. A video in a **culinary** YouTube series might include how to

   A. make a Moroccan eggplant salad.

   B. identify authentic 19th-century music boxes.

   C. design floral bouquets for special events.

   D. choose a good processor for a computer.

3. It would be obvious that a person is **feigning** interest in a lecture if she is

    A. looking directly at the speaker.

    B. asking questions about the topic.

    C. taking extensive notes.

    D. looking at the clock.

4. What does the word *own* refer to in the following sentence?

    "Rappers like Eminem, Jay-Z, and Tupac have mentioned in interviews that they studied the dictionary to develop large vocabularies; Snoop, on the other hand, created his own."

    A. vocabulary

    B. interview

    C. identity

    D. dictionary

5. Which of the following would be a **malicious** reason to ignore a phone call?

    A. You are in the middle of watching a movie or television show.

    B. You want to make the other person feel unimportant.

    C. You need to concentrate on your work without interruption.

    D. You left your phone in the other room and didn't hear it ring.

EXERCISE 5 / ROOTS, PREFIXES, AND SUFFIXES

Answer the questions below that are designed to help you arrive at some conclusions about word families and origins.

Roots: *voc/vok*, "to call"

      lud, "to play; to escape; to mock"

1. What common suffix could be added to **overwhelm** and **feign** that would add "the act or process of" to each definition? _____

2. The suffixes –*ism* and –*ity* indicate that the word is usually what part of speech? _____

   The suffixes –*ary* and –*ous* indicate that the word is usually what part of speech? _____

   The suffix –*ize* indicates that the word is usually what part of speech? _____

3. Two words below have the prefix *e*–, meaning "out." Define each word. Then, explain how we might get such a meaning from this prefix and root.

   A. The poem **evoked** powerful memories of home for Sami.

      _____

   B. No matter how fast the little dog runs, the squirrels always **elude** her.

      _____

4. Build a word from the given prefix and suffix, include the root, and then match it to its definition.

   The prefix *ad*– means "to call, to speak."

   The suffix –*ate* means "someone."

   "someone who speaks on behalf of or defends" = _____

VOCABULARY

abate	*verb*	to lessen the intensity of
abhor	*verb*	to despise; to hate
abolition	*noun*	the act of stopping or ending something
accelerate	*verb*	to speed up over time
adjunct	*adj.*	extra or additional, but not essential
advocate	*verb*	to recommend; to speak in favor of
affiliate	*noun*	an associate
affront	*noun*	a personally offensive action or word; a lack of respect for
aghast	*adj.*	feeling great dismay or horror
alacrity	*noun*	liveliness; willingness; eagerness
alienate	*verb*	to make others act in an unfriendly way
allude	*verb*	to hint at; to refer to indirectly
aloof	*adj.*	reserved; distant
amalgamate	*verb*	to combine
antagonize	*verb*	to deliberately irritate
anthem	*noun*	a powerful song, usually with a message
aplomb	*noun*	self-confidence
apparel	*noun*	clothing; attire
articulate	*adj.*	well-spoken; spoken clearly
atrocious	*adj.*	awful, horrible
attribute	*verb*	to associate a particular characteristic or event to
auditory	*adj.*	relating to hearing
bandy	*verb*	to give and take quickly in conversation; to toss back and forth

bane	*noun*	the cause of ruin, harm, or distress
bedlam	*noun*	a state of confusion or chaos
beget	*verb*	to produce; to be the parent of
belated	*adj.*	occurring later than expected or anticipated; overdue
benefactor	*noun*	a person who helps another person in need; a contributor
bias	*noun*	a prejudiced view
blatant	*adj.*	obvious; standing out
boisterous	*adj.*	loud, rowdy
buoyant	*adj.*	cheerful or invigorating
callous	*adj.*	insensitive toward others; uncaring
capitalize	*verb*	to take advantage; to use
captivate	*verb*	to fascinate someone or something; to enchant
caricature	*noun*	an exaggerated portrayal of one's features
carnage	*noun*	bloody and extensive slaughter
catalyst	*noun*	a person, thing, or agent that speeds up or stimulates a result, reaction, or change
catholic	*adj.*	universal; wide-ranging
cavort	*verb*	to leap about in a lively manner; to romp
celebrity	*noun*	a very well-known public figure
censor	*verb*	to remove offensive parts from something
charisma	*noun*	a great appeal or attraction for others; personal magnetism
chauvinism	*noun*	the belief in the superiority of one's own country, race, or gender
conform	*verb*	to behave in a socially acceptable way
contemptible	*adj.*	worthy of disgrace
controversy	*noun*	a dispute about something
conventional	*adj.*	usual; going along with accepted standards

culinary	*adj.*	relating to cooking
debatable	*adj.*	open to questioning; arguable; disputable
decadence	*noun*	moral decay
deface	*verb*	to vandalize or disfigure something
defunct	*adj.*	no longer in existence; no longer working
dejected	*adj.*	feeling depressed
delude	*verb*	to mislead; to fool
denigrate	*verb*	to ruin the reputation of; to speak ill of
denounce	*verb*	to condemn openly
diction	*noun*	a clear, precise, and effective selection of words
disrespect	*noun*	a lack of respect
distort	*verb*	to change the shape or form of
dominate	*verb*	to control; to rule
elite	*adj.*	best or choice; superior; exclusive
eloquent	*adj.*	passionate and expressive when speaking or writing
elude	*verb*	to escape notice; to get away from
embezzle	*verb*	to steal money placed in one's trust
emissary	*noun*	one sent on a special mission to represent others
ensue	*verb*	to result from; to come after
entity	*noun*	an independent being; a real and independent existence
envisage	*verb*	to form a mental picture
evolve	*verb*	to develop and change
exhilarated	*adj.*	feeling thrilled or excited; enlivened
exploit	*verb*	to take advantage of; to use for an advantage
facade	*noun*	a deceptive outward appearance

fallible	*adj.*	capable of error
farcical	*adj.*	absurd; ridiculous
fatalistic	*adj.*	believing that all things in life are determined by fate
feasible	*adj.*	able to be done easily; achievable
feign	*verb*	to pretend
felony	*noun*	a crime punishable by jail time or death
fidelity	*noun*	faithfulness; loyalty to a person, religion, ideology, or concept; accuracy in detail
flagrant	*adj.*	obvious; very noticeable; outrageous
flaunt	*verb*	to show off and display proudly
foresight	*noun*	the ability to plan in advance
formidable	*adj.*	powerful, strong, and having the ability to cause fear
frivolous	*adj.*	unimportant; silly
futile	*adj.*	useless
gait	*noun*	the manner of walking
genealogy	*noun*	family history; the study of ancestry
genesis	*noun*	the beginning; the origin
glamorize	*verb*	to make something seem more interesting, exciting, or attractive
glorify	*verb*	to make something seem much better than it really is
gratify	*verb*	to please
guile	*noun*	slyness and cunning
gyrate	*verb*	to rotate; to spin
hapless	*adj.*	unfortunate or unlucky
haughty	*adj.*	arrogant; proud
hilarity	*noun*	happiness, joy
homage	*noun*	honor or respect for someone or something

hone	*verb*	to sharpen; to refine
humility	*noun*	a humble opinion of one's own self-importance
idolize	*verb*	to have excessive admiration for or devotion to
illusion	*noun*	something that is not what it appears to be or gives a false sense of reality
impede	*verb*	to hinder; to obstruct
impel	*verb*	to push into motion, usually by some outside force
impersonate	*verb*	to imitate
impertinent	*adj.*	rude and disrespectful
impoverished	*adj.*	poor
incite	*verb*	to cause to happen
inclusive	*adj.*	including a large number of people or objects in a group
insight	*noun*	an ability to understand the truth of something
introvert	*noun*	a person who is most comfortable in quiet and private surroundings
jargon	*noun*	words used by a specific group of individuals that can be difficult for others to understand
laborious	*adj.*	requiring a great deal of time and effort
lament	*verb*	to mourn; to show sadness or regret
lampoon	*verb*	to ridicule or attack by using satire
lavish	*adj.*	fancy, extravagant
legitimate	*adj.*	lawful; acceptable
lethal	*adj.*	deadly, fatal
licentious	*adj.*	morally or sexually unrestrained; indifferent to laws or rules
magnitude	*noun*	the size or degree of something
malicious	*adj.*	intentionally causing harm
manipulate	*verb*	to skillfully and cleverly control a situation or another individual
memorable	*adj.*	worth remembering; notable

mesmerized	*adj.*	hypnotized; captivated
milestone	*noun*	an event or occurrence that represents something important
misogyny	*adj.*	a dislike of or prejudice against women
mitigate	*verb*	to make less severe
momentary	*adj.*	lasting only a short while; fleeting
morality	*noun*	a belief in proper standards of behavior
nadir	*noun*	the lowest point
naïve	*adj.*	innocent; unaware
narcissistic	*adj.*	conceited; having excessive self-absorption
nefarious	*adj.*	very wicked
negotiate	*verb*	to bring about a result by way of discussion
neophyte	*noun*	a beginner
nepotism	*noun*	favoritism shown to a relative
nominate	*verb*	to formally recommend for an award, election, or high honor
noteworthy	*adj.*	interesting; important; unusual
notorious	*adj.*	known to be wicked or evil
nucleus	*noun*	the central or most important part of an object or group
obnoxious	*adj.*	extremely unpleasant
obscene	*adj.*	offensive and indecent
ogre	*noun*	a monster; a bossy person
ordeal	*noun*	an unpleasant or particularly traumatic experience
ostentatious	*adj.*	overly fancy
overwhelmed	*adj.*	overcome by force or numbers
pariah	*noun*	an outcast; someone who is not welcome
parry	*verb*	to turn aside in a defensive way; to deflect

patron	*noun*	an individual who supports another person or organization
penchant	*noun*	a strong liking for
perceive	*verb*	to interpret or understand
persevere	*verb*	to steadily proceed in a course of action
perspective	*noun*	a mental view or outlook; a way of understanding something
pertinent	*adj.*	having a direct relevance to something
pessimistic	*adj.*	anticipating negative outcomes
phenomenal	*adj.*	amazing; extraordinary; unexpected
pinnacle	*noun*	the highest point
plausible	*adj.*	reasonable or believable; probable
prelude	*noun*	something that precedes
prevalent	*adj.*	widespread
progression	*noun*	a sequence moving forward
prosecute	*verb*	to put on trial
prosper	*verb*	to be successful, especially financially
provoke	*verb*	to cause an action to take place
queue	*noun*	an ordered line
radical	*adj.*	very different from the normal or acceptable
random	*adj.*	without a definite plan or purpose
refrain	*verb*	to choose not do something
reprimand	*verb*	to criticize or express disapproval of
repulsive	*adj.*	disgusting, awful
respectable	*adj.*	worthy of esteem and praise
retard	*verb*	to slow down or delay progress
rift	*noun*	a split

righteous	*adj.*	morally upstanding
segment	*noun*	a section or small part
snub	*verb*	to reject and disapprove by ignoring
subordinate	*noun*	someone in a lower position or standing
superficial	*adj.*	without depth or importance
taboo	*adj.*	a restraint or restriction set up by society
tempo	*noun*	the speed at which a piece of music should be played
tolerate	*verb*	to endure unpleasantness
vivid	*adj.*	producing intense feelings or clear, detailed pictures in the mind